T

NCER

I

Santo Nic

CAPE VE

A

30°　　　　　　　　15°　　　　　　　　0°

Match

THE STORY OF

DR. BOMBARD'S

65-DAY SOLITARY

ATLANTIC CROSSING

IN A COLLAPSIBLE

LIFE RAFT

Match

Jean Ferré

THE VOYAGE OF THE
HERETIQUE

by Dr. Alain Bombard

TRANSLATED BY BRIAN CONNELL

SIMON AND SCHUSTER · NEW YORK

Barbados Advocate

L'Illustration

Library of Congress Catalog Card Number: 54-5813
Dewey Decimal Classification Number: 508.3

MANUFACTURED IN THE UNITED STATES OF AMERICA
VAIL-BALLOU PRESS, INC., BINGHAMTON, N.Y.

CONTENTS

FOREWORD   vii

THE PLAN TAKES SHAPE   1

  1. Sponsor   3
  2. Purpose   8
  3. Equipment   20

MEDITERRANEAN   39

  4. Departure   41
  5. On the High Seas   57
  6. Capsize   72
  7. Tangier Interlude   79

ATLANTIC   91

  8. Lone Voyager   93
  9. Casablanca-Las Palmas   103
 10. Temptations of Terra Firma   ' 111
 11. Atlantic Challenge   120

12. Mid-Passage   156
13. Longitude   168
14. Arakaka and Arrival   188
15. A Landfall   204

CONCLUSIONS   211

FOREWORD

EARLY ONE MORNING in the spring of 1951 I was asleep in the residents' quarters of the hospital at Boulogne-sur-Mer when the telephone rang:

"Is that the house surgeon?"

"Yes, what is it?"

"A ship has been wrecked on the Carnot mole."

"I'll come at once."

Grumbling to myself, with no inkling of how serious the accident was, I dressed quickly and hurried down to the casualty ward. No patients had yet arrived. I asked the night porter what had happened and he told me that a trawler, the *Notre-Dame-de-Peyragues,* from the little port of Equihem, had missed her course in the mist and had hit the outer end of the Carnot mole. This is the outer breakwater of the harbor; very dangerous in bad weather, but easy to scale at other times, as there are ladders every twenty yards along its face. The weather was cold, but the sea was calm and I was not unduly anxious.

Then came the sound of the siren of one of the fire brigade vehicles. The double doors were thrust open and I took a couple of steps toward the entrance, full of my own importance. . . . I shall never forget the terrible spectacle of those forty-three men piled one on top of the other, like dislocated puppets, their feet bare, and each still wearing a life belt. In spite of all our efforts, we failed to revive a single one. An error of navigation lasting a few moments had caused forty-three deaths and seventy-eight orphans.

I think it was at that moment that the full measure of tragedy conjured up by the word shipwreck was brought home to me. The seed was sown for what developed into the expedition of *L'Hérétique*. Shipwreck became for me the very expression of human misery, a synonym for despair, hunger, and thirst. Boulogne alone lost between a hundred and a hundred and fifty fishermen every year. I discovered that throughout the world in peacetime more than two hundred thousand men—and women—suffered the same fate. More than a quarter of them, having survived disaster and reached the boats, died shortly afterward in mortal agony.

For some time I had been making a study of the resistance of the human organism to privations. I was convinced that it was possible for an individual to survive far beyond the limits normally assigned by physiological science. I had paid particular attention to the case histories of political deportees, prisoners, and undernourished populations. But, with my background as a doctor, for whom the teachings of science remain a dead letter unless they can find practical application, my theoretical studies only seemed to lead to the question: "What use can be made of this knowledge?"

The problem of shipwrecked survivors found its natural place in such a study. It had one special characteristic: the external conditions contributing to this particular form of human misery were not, as in the case of prisoners and the like, due to the malice of man, against which there is no defense, nor to famine, as in India and China, with only limited possibilities of help, but to a natural element, dangerous without doubt, but nevertheless rich in the necessities of life sufficient to insure survival until the arrival of aid or the sighting of land.

There are nearly two hundred times as many living organisms in a cubic yard of water as in the same amount of earth. Although the sea represents a constant danger to the castaway, it is not malicious and above all not sterile. The conquest of fear and the search for sustenance should not present insurmountable difficulties. That was my basic premise as far as the environment was concerned. I had also become convinced that in their studies of the capacity of the human organism to survive in such circumstances, the physiologists had not taken sufficiently into account the power of the will and its influence on physical reactions. In their different spheres it is only necessary to recall the fasts of Gandhi, the voyage of Captain Bligh, who lived for forty days on eight days' provisions, sustained by his hate for his mutinous crew, and the Polar expeditions of Scott and Amundsen. It is not a question of survival being possible in certain defined conditions, but rather, to use the formula so dear to mathematicians, "other things being equal" (thus allowing latitude for the effect of courage and the will to live), survival is certain if specific physical conditions are met.

I went back to my statistics: could something be done to save those fifty thousand people who die every year in lifeboats, and if so what? At first, the classic stories of shipwreck which I then began to study seemed to rule out the possibility of any additional factor turning the scale:

The frigate *La Méduse* was lost on July 2, 1816, on a sandbank about a hundred miles off the African coast. One hundred and forty-nine of the survivors—passengers, soldiers, and a few officers—had to trust themselves to a hastily constructed raft towed by the ship's boats. The tow broke in circumstances which have never been explained, and the raft was abandoned to the fury of the Atlantic. There were six barrels of wine and two of fresh water on board. The raft was not sighted again until twelve days later. By then, there were only fifteen survivors, ten of whom died shortly after rescue.

On April 15, 1912, the liner *Titanic* hit an iceberg in the North Atlantic and sank in a few hours. When the first relief ships arrived, three hours after the liner had disappeared, a number of people had either died or gone mad in the lifeboats. Significantly, no child under the age of ten was included among those who had paid for their terror with madness and for their madness with death. The children were still at the age of reason.

These examples confirmed for me the overwhelming importance of morale. Statistics show that ninety per cent of the survivors of shipwreck die within three days, yet it takes longer than that to perish of hunger and thirst. When his ship goes down, a man's whole universe goes with it. Because he no longer has a deck under his feet, his courage and reason abandon him. Even if he reaches a lifeboat, he is not necessarily safe. He sits, slumped, contemplating his misery, and can hardly be said to be alive. Helpless in the night, chilled by sea and wind, terrified by the solitude, by the noise and by the silence, it takes less than three days for him to surrender his life.

How many castaways through the ages have become stiff and sudden corpses, killed, not by the sea, not by hunger or thirst, but by their own terror? I became convinced that most of them had died long before the physical and physiological conditions had of themselves become fatal. How was one to combat despair, a far more ruthless and efficient killer than any physical factor?

ALAIN BOMBARD

PART ONE

THE PLAN TAKES SHAPE

CHAPTER 1

Sponsor

Toward the end of Sepember, 1951, one of my competitors in that year's attempts to swim the English channel (an unsuccessful one on my part, since I gave up when I was half a mile from the English coast after thirteen hours and forty-five minutes of swimming), Jean van Hemsbergen, suggested that we go for a sail together. He was trying out a new type of lifeboat. As soon as my turn of duty was finished at the hospital, I joined him on the beach, where I found him about to launch an inflatable rubber dinghy. The floats were shaped like a horseshoe, the open end closed by a wooden stern board. It was the forerunner, on a smaller scale, of *L'Hérétique*, the boat in which I made the voyage which is described in this book. We set off about four o'clock in the afternoon to test the outboard motor.

It was a lovely day.

"What do you say we try and make for Folkestone?" Jean suggested. It seemed a fine idea, so we set off to the north-northwest, steering for the South Foreland, picking up the flashes of its lighthouse as night fell. The wind rose and the sea became quite rough, but the *Hitchhiker,* as the dinghy was called, behaved admirably, and we entered Folkestone harbor about eleven o'clock. I had no passport, but the British authorities did not raise any difficulties.

The weather quickly deteriorated, and soon it was blowing half a gale out of the North Sea. In spite of the confidence we had in the dinghy, we thought it better to wait for the wind to die down. We did venture outside the harbor once, but it seemed madness to continue, so we turned back. The gale showed no signs of abating and I realized the hospital would be getting worried. I had already sent off a telegram to tell them where I was, but I had to get back for duty as my internship did not end until October 1. Scorning all advice, we decided to brave the sea and set off at nine o'clock on the morning of September 23. We almost gave up at the harbor bar, but the experience to be gained seemed to justify the risk. After all, survivors do not choose the weather in which to be shipwrecked, and nine times out of ten when they have to take to the boats it is in the middle of a storm.

We met the sea head-on and expected at any moment that the motor would be swamped. But everything went well; *Hitchhiker* rode the waves magnificently. The Channel, normally so full of traffic, was absolutely deserted. After several narrow escapes we reached the beach at Wissant about six o'clock in the afternoon. The dinghy had proved its worth.

We were met on our arrival by a man who was to become for some time my patron and backer. He was a Dutchman, well known as an expert in salvage and lifesaving equipment, a big fellow, some six feet tall and weighing all of three hundred and fifty pounds. He had a fine open face, great powers of persuasion, and a frank nature. Or at least so it appeared to me at the time.

We took to each other at once, and in the course of our conversations over the next few days he put forward the idea of establishing a grant which would enable me to work out in detail in a laboratory my half-formed theories on the possibilities of survival at sea. I was to establish scientifically the minimum necessary intake of food and drink, and then we would all three embark on a sea voyage to prove that we had found ways and means of saving future castaways from despair. I was also to map out a possible course, while our backer rounded up the necessary equipment. We decided that I should start my studies at the Museum of Oceanography in Monaco and that our expedition would take place about the end of the year.

Fate then took a hand. I began my experiments earlier than I expected by becoming an involuntary castaway. Before leaving for Monaco, van Hemsbergen and I were due to make a quick trip to England for the wedding of one of our friends. On Wednesday, October 3, while we were trying out a new motor in the dinghy off Wissant, it broke down about three miles north-northwest of Cape Gris-Nez, and we started to drift. We had planned to make only a short trial and we had on board neither sail nor any alternative means of propulsion. The wind was from the north-northeast and drove us along for two days and three nights with no hope of approaching land. Although the coast was out of sight, we knew we must be drifting roughly parallel to it and that after the mouth of the Somme it turned west again, so we were not unduly worried. With any luck we should end up between St. Valéry and Dieppe. Finally, on Friday, about nine o'clock in the morning, we sighted a trawler, the *Notre-Dame du Clergé*, and tried to head toward it by using the dinghy's waterproof cover as a makeshift sail. Modest resources are often the way out of great difficulties, a lesson which was not lost on me. For two days van Hemsbergen had drunk nothing at all. I, on the other hand, had taken small quantities of sea water to quench my thirst, knowing that in such proportions I ran no risk. The only food we had was a pound of butter, which one of us had brought on board by pure chance—hardly the ideal thirst-quencher.

The trawler picked us up. My companion buried his head in a bucket of fresh water. Convinced I must be thirsty, I did the same, but at the second swallow I stopped. I was simply not thirsty. Thanks to my regime of sea water, I had not become dehydrated and felt no need for liquids. It was a striking example of the manner in which force of habit can influence the organism to the point of inducing an apparent need where none really exists.

Three days later I read the following in one of the local newspapers: "Alain Bombard picked up half-dead from hunger near St. Valéry." People were already beginning to fictionalize my story. Yet the two men who hurried to catch a plane at Le Touquet in order not to miss a wedding in Britain hardly looked like corpses. Nevertheless, the authorities were on our trail. I was soon involved in the first act of a scenario which provided, at the most unexpected moments, a number of vexatious episodes both during my preparations and the actual voyage. I have called it, with apologies to Courteline, the Comic Interlude:

The first scene took place in an office full of desks, each piled high with papers. Behind one of them a full naval captain sat. I was seated in front of him like a naughty schoolboy.

"Do you realize," he pontificated, "that you have committed an offense in leaving territorial waters without a navigation permit?"

"But a certain latitude is granted to small boats."

"That is so, but only to those described as beach craft, and they are still not permitted to leave territorial waters."

"Are they forbidden outside these limits?"

"There is nothing in the regulations about that."

"Well, then?"

But my interrogator put an end to the interview by saying: "In any case it is quite impossible to overlook your continual infringements."

"Are you not going to take into account the fact that I was only a passenger and that the owner was on board?"

"I am under no obligation to answer you; I will let you know my decision in due course."

We parted on bad terms, but, as at the end of each of these

episodes, there was always some compensation. In the waiting room I ran into another naval captain, a real seaman this time, Captain Maupeou, who greeted me warmly and said: "Well done, old man."

CHAPTER 2

Purpose

I ARRIVED in Monaco on October 19 and went to pay my respects at the Museum of Oceanography, with a request that I be placed on their list of research workers and be given a laboratory in which to begin my studies. I was received by the deputy director, M. Belloc, whose interest in my experiments and whose friendly assistance never wavered. I obtained all the facilities I needed the first day and wasted no time in getting down to work.

It will be easier for readers to follow the events described in this book if they will bear with me while I explain what was known, and what was thought to be known on the subject of saving lives at sea when I started my detailed studies. The expedition itself, first through part of the Mediterranean and then across the Atlantic, was merely an attempt to prove in practice what I had satisfied myself in the laboratory was the true situation. But unless I can explain now exactly what I was setting out to prove, the incidents of the voyage lose their point. It is essential to state certain facts concerning nutrition, the reactions of the human organism, the contents of the sea, and the characteristics of certain fish. All this had to be studied before I set off, and although it has been suggested to me that the general reader might be happier if this information was printed in an appendix at the end of the book—advice tendered in good faith and given my serious consideration—I have decided that this is the right place. This research work formed the basis of my whole voyage and this knowledge sustained me when everything seemed to go wrong. Although those who wish to join me in my adventure may wish to skip to the section entitled Mediterranean, they will find they will need to return here to complete the picture.

Shipwrecks fall into two categories: those that occur on the coast and those on the high seas. Of the two hundred thousand human beings who die every year as the result of accidents at sea, just over half lose their lives on the coasts of the world. For the survivors, assistance is usually at hand through the devoted labors of the Coast Guard facilities in each country.

On the high seas, the situation is different. Here about fifty thousand unfortunates die each year, more or less at the moment their ship goes down. That leaves another fifty thousand who might be saved. They, in their turn, fall into two categories:

There are two sorts of ship. First, the big liners and naval vessels in permanent radio contact with land the whole time they are at sea. If one of them founders, everyone knows to within a few miles exactly where the disaster has happened and other ships hurry to the rescue. For survivors of such ships, the knowledge that rescue is a certainty should provide a "morale injection" sufficient to avoid the fate of so many of the *Titanic* survivors. Under these conditions, the problem of facing a prolonged fight for survival is practically nonexistent.

Then come the other types of vessel, cargo boats, tramps, deep-sea trawlers, and fishing boats in general. Normally they have only a fixed radio rendezvous with land, every six, every twelve, sometimes every twenty-four hours. Between each signal they can cover a considerable distance. If something happens to them, the exact position of the catastrophe is difficult to determine and the lot of the survivors is correspondingly grim. These are the men, and women, who were always uppermost in my thoughts and whom my experiment was designed to help. To my dismay I discovered that relatively little is done for them. If their ship goes down they are considered as lost. Only in the most favorable circumstances does a search last for as long as ten days. After ten days it has become a norm of our civilization to abandon the search on the grounds that there is no longer any hope of finding them alive. The explanation given is that neither human being nor equipment can be expected to hold out longer than that. My object was to give these unfortunates a better chance of reaching land. Several thousand widows less per year seemed to me an objective fully justifying the risk of one life.

My research work came under five headings. I looked up every possible reference on:

1) The history of previous shipwrecks and the lessons to be learned from them.
2) The case histories of survivors.
3) Fish and their chemical composition.
4) The various methods of catching fish.
5) The study of favorable winds and currents.

At the same time I tried out on myself in the laboratory various experiments with abnormal food, while van Hemsbergen, who joined me, concentrated chiefly on the study of the best type of craft for our purpose.

The whole ground had to be carefully covered. Over a period of six months the day's work varied from the chemical analysis of sea water to a minute study of the various types of plankton, together with laborious analyses of the chemical composition of different species of fish. I took as my basic premise the fact that although a lifeboat or life raft may be equipped in theory with every conceivable type of apparatus, much of it might have been washed overboard by the time it was necessary to use it.

Almost on the first day I managed to turn up a basic document in the latest issue of the *Bulletin des amis du musée océano-graphique*. It was a reprint of a report made to the Academy of Sciences on December 17, 1888, by Prince Albert I of Monaco, the founder of the museum:

"I judge it useful to communicate to the Academy," the Prince had written, "an account of certain striking investigations into ocean fauna carried out in conjunction with other scientific studies over the last four years by *L'Hirondelle*. Experiments during 1888 proved conclusively that an abundance of sea fauna could be caught during the night hours.

"A fine silk net about eight feet in diameter, towed on the surface for about half an hour, always brought in a considerable quantity of fish (Scopelidæ) and about seventy cubic centimeters of edible organic matter.

"A simple landing net about twenty inches wide of the same material, plunged at night into one of the shoals of jelly fish often encountered in the Atlantic, would bring up about fifteen cubic centimeters of the small crustaceans (*Hyperia latreillei*) which are usually to be found in their company.

"In the area of the Sargasso Sea there is a whole family of marine life to be found hidden amongst the fronds of this floating seaweed. It is made up of both crustaceans and fish, in even greater quantities than those just mentioned, but they are often not perceived at first glance because of their similarity in coloring to the weeds themselves.

"During the months of July and August last, *L'Hirondelle* made a study of the occurrence of tunny fish up to a distance of six hundred leagues to the west and southwest of Europe: two lines with artificial bait caught fifty-three tunny fish with a total weight of 908 lbs.

"Submerged wrecks and flotsam, sufficiently old to have attracted barnacles, are always accompanied by quite sizable fish. Six such objects were inspected in July and September, and it was possible to catch twenty-eight sea perch with a combined weight of 303 lbs. During this and previous seasons there was no difficulty in catching almost any amount of these fish (300 lbs. on one day alone) without seeming to diminish the numbers round the wreck in any way."

This report made it quite clear that shipwrecked survivors in the North Atlantic, and probably any other ocean in the temperate regions, could escape death by starvation if they had the following equipment:

1) One or several nets of straining cloth, between three and six feet in diameter, on about sixty feet of line, in order to pick up the smaller sea fauna.

2) Several fishing lines about 150 feet in length, ending in three casts of brass wire attached to a large hook, with some sort of artificial bait, for tunny fish.

3) A small spear or harpoon with which to catch sea perch in the neighborhood of wrecks and a few brightly polished hooks, which these fish will often take without any bait.

4) A large harpoon with which to catch larger fish.

The Prince ended his report by stating firmly that with this knowledge and equipment it should be possible for the survivors of a shipwreck to maintain life until help arrived.

My next problem was to show that the sea not only provided food but a sufficient and balanced diet. The ocean supplies three things: sea water, fish, and plankton. The latter group is made up of the millions of tiny microscopic creatures which are to be found in any sample of fresh or salt water. They fall into two main groups: planktonic animals, or zooplankton (living microorganisms and fish eggs); and planktonic plants, or phytoplankton, made up of algæ or microscopic seaweed. Plankton is of enormous biological importance, as all animal life in the sea is ultimately dependent on it for existence. It is, moreover, the principal food of whales, the largest existing mammals.

The average composition of sea water (according to Jean Rouch's *Traité d'océanographie Physique,* published by Flammarion) is:

COMPOSITION OF SEA WATER
(per kilogram)

Na Cl	27.3	grams
Mg Cl$_2$	3.4	"
Mg SO$_4$	2.0	"
Ca SO$_4$	1.3	"
K Cl	0.6	"
Ca CO$_3$	0.1	"
H$_2$O	965.3	"
	1000.0	"

A chemical analysis of fish shows that its principal elements are water, proteins, and fats. According to Creac'h, *Les Protides liquides du poisson,* the types of fish most likely to be encountered during the course of my voyage and their chemical content are:

PRINCIPAL CONSTITUENTS OF FISH
(percentages by weight)

FISH	WATER	PROTEINS	FATS
ray	76.8–82.2	18.2–24.2	0.1–1.6
basking shark	68.0	15.2	16.0
dolphin	77.00–78.89	17.25–19.00	1.00–3.31
ray's bream	78.90	18.42	0.34
sardine	78.34	16.3–21.0	2.0–12.0
anchovy	76.19	21.92	1.11
bonito	67.50–69.27	18.52–24.00	7.00–12.46
bass	77.00–79.94	18.53–19.96	0.84–2.50

FISH	WATER	PROTEINS	FATS
mullet	75.6	19.5	3.9
mackerel	68.84–74.27	17.59–23.10	5.14–8.36
tunny	58.5	27.0	13.0
fish roe	48.80–78.31	11.5–45.9	1.16–16.20

With plankton, the composition is clearly much more variable and unpredictable. I spent the greater proportion of my time in trying to track down some of the elements of nutrition which I knew were still lacking. I was in the position of a man who has been given a limited amount of material and is told: "With that you must build a house." I set to work.

The principal problem was water. Everyone knows that drinking is more important than eating. Ten days without water result inevitably in death, but a man can survive for thirty days without food. Where was I to get my fresh water? I soon reached the conclusion that the fish themselves were going to provide me with all I needed. The previous table shows that a fish is made up of between fifty and eighty per cent by weight of water. Moreover, it is fresh water, and this was the liquid with which I intended to quench my thirst.

Have you ever had to eat fish which some careless cook has forgotten to season? It is completely insipid. I proved by analysis that the flesh of fish is greatly inferior in sodium chloride (common salt) to that of mammals—with one or two exceptions to which I shall refer again when considering the subject of proteins. If only I could extract the liquid from the flesh I would get all the water I needed from between six and seven pounds of fish a day. The problem was to extract it, but that was a practical rather than a laboratory problem.

But what was to happen if I caught no fish? That is often the case during the three or four days after a ship founders, before the survivors have organized themselves. This is the critical period. If there is nothing to drink, death from dehydration occurs within ten days, after an almost regular decline in the body's water content. Any supply of water or fresh liquid which then becomes available, if it does not exceed the day's basic requirement, means that the survivor's water content remains at the same level as it was on the day he started drinking again. The body thus is not restored to its normal condition. The essential thing is therefore to maintain the body's water content at its proper level during those first few days before fish can be caught. The only solution is to drink sea water.

Sea water is dangerous. That is something everyone knows. Consumed in large quantities it causes death by nephritis (inflammation of the kidneys). What is to be done then? The answer lies in a study of its composition. The most important component is sodium chloride. I therefore made up my mind that I would consume the permissible daily intake of salt by swallowing it in sea water. This meant that I could absorb between 800 and 900 grams of salt water a day. The chief thing I had to worry about was its effect on the Malpighian corpuscles. These form the first filter in the kidneys and have to work hardest when there is an abnormal concentration of mineral salts. The question was how long the corpuscles could continue to work without damage. As far as I could make out this was about five days, after which the danger of nephritis becomes acute.

"What about the other chemicals in sea water?" you may ask.

I made some additional analyses on this problem. France, as everyone knows, is famous for its mineral springs. My figures showed that the quantity of sea water I had in mind contained the following mineral salts:

The same amount of magnesium chloride ($MgCl_2$) as in a quart of Salies water

The same quantity of magnesium sulphate ($Mg\ SO_4$) as in a quart of Montmirail water

The same amount of calcium sulphate ($Ca\ SO_4$) as in a quart of Contrexéville water

As much potassium chloride (K Cl) as in a quart of Bourbon water

And the same quantity of calcium carbonate (Ca CO₃) as in a quart of Vichy "Grande Grille" water

The water problem therefore seemed to be solved. The next thing to be considered in detail was the intake of food. I had to devise a diet which would provide me with the necessary number of calories, paying due attention to the three main classes of foods, proteins, fats, and carbohydrates.

The table showing the chemical analysis of fish proves that as far as quantity is concerned, ample proteins are available. But the problem is complicated by the fact that the human organism makes highly selective demands and has to have a certain type of protein. One variety, called the amino acids, is absolutely essential. For these there is no substitute. All of them are to be found in fish. The table shows the distribution in different species of the ten amino acids which chiefly concern us here:

AMINO ACID CONTENT OF FISH
(in Centigrams Per 100 Grams)

Fish	Amino Acid									
	Arginine	Histidine	Isoleucine	Leucine	Lysine	Methionine	Phenylalanine	Threonine	Tryptophan	Valine
mackerel	5.8	3.8	5.2	7.2	8.1	2.7	3.5	4.9	1.0	5.4
herring	5.5	2.4	4.9	7.1	7.8	2.7	3.4	4.4	0.8	5.0
sardine	5.1	4.7	4.6	7.2	8.4	2.8	3.7	4.3	1.0	5.2
tunny	5.3	5.7	4.7	7.2	8.3	2.8	3.5	4.5	1.0	5.1
shrimp	9.4	2.2	5.3	8.5	8.5	3.4	4.5	4.1	1.0	5.1

On the other hand, there were certain types of protein of which I had to beware, particularly the ureides and purine bases. These are only present in quantity in the cartilaginous fishes, such as rays and sharks, which I would have to treat with extreme circumspection.

As far as fats were concerned, the only question was to know whether I would find phospholipids, that is to say, fats containing phosphorus, such as lecithin. (Egg yolks are normally an important source.) Here it is necessary for me to say only that abundant fats of the right type are valuable in all fish.

But then came the most decisive factor of all, that of carbohydrates and sugar. As far as the human being is concerned, these come from two sources, exogenous, that is to say, consumed in food, or endogenous, manufactured by the body itself. There seemed few enough external sources of supply. Where was I to find sugar in the sea? It existed in quantity in the planktonic plants, but was it of a type which could be assimilated by the human organism?

The carbohydrates fall into three main groups:

1) The monosaccharides, which can be assimilated as they are, characterized by the fact that their molecule contains six carbon atoms (C_6). The most typical is glucose.

2) The disaccharides, with twelve atoms of carbon (C_{12}) such as saccharose, *i.e.*, cane or beet sugar. They cannot be digested as they are but have to go through a process of hydrolysis during digestion which splits them into two molecules of C_6 sugar.

3) The polysaccharides, carbohydrates characterized by eighteen or more carbon atoms in multiples of six in the molecule. Many carbohydrates of this group, such as cellulose, cannot be absorbed by the system. They pass through it unchanged, as they cannot be hydrolyzed into the assimilable C_6 components. Unfortunately, plankton contains only sugar of this third category.

The livers of many fish generate glucose. However, if I ate too much liver, I ran the risk of making myself very ill because liver contains Vitamins A and D, two very dangerous substances if taken in excess. It therefore seemed that I was going to have to rely on my own body manufacturing the carbohydrates I needed. In normal circumstances the human organism is capable of doing this providing it has a sufficient supply of meat, fat—and a considerable quantity of water. I was in a vicious circle, and only practical experience could give the real answer. I had one encouraging example, that of the Eskimos, who for six months of the Polar winter eat only meat and fat and drink melted sea water ice, without seeming to suffer any serious consequences to their digestions.

I still needed minute quantities of certain other substances, the famous vitamins. Infinitesimal as the amounts involved are, their absence can cause serious illness—the deficiency diseases or avitaminosis. Too much of them can have equally serious effects, resulting in hypervitaminosis. Four of them, vitamins A, B, C, and D, are absolutely essential and it is not possible to do without them even for a short time. For the remainder, the margin of safety is considerably wider.

Vitamin A and vitamin D, as I have noted, are extremely abundant in fish oil. (I do not need to remind readers of their experiences as children with cod liver oil.) Vitamins B 1 and B 2 are abundantly present in the flesh of fish, in which, however, as far as I know, no one has ever detected any trace of vitamin B 12, the anti-pernicious anemia factor. The margin of safety in this case is again quite wide, although the anemic state in which I finally arrived would seem to indicate that vitamin B 12 is only found at sea in very limited quantities.

Even with these considerations out of the way, there remained that scourge of sailors through the ages, scurvy. This is a deficiency disease due to the absence of Vitamin C, present in fresh fruit, green vegetables and plant life in general. How was I to solve this problem?

My reasoning was this: animals are divided into two types, those that manufacture their own ascorbic acid (vitamin C) and those which take it in the form of food. Now the whale is one of the animals which has to find an outside source for its ascorbic acid and it feeds exclusively on plankton or on the minute crustaceans which themselves feed on plankton. It therefore seemed certain that plankton would provide my source of vitamin C, and this I verified by chemical analysis.

There seemed every possibility of making up a balanced diet. I had my vitamins A, B, C, and D and, as far as their calorie content was concerned, all the proteins and fats I needed. There was only one worry, and that a major one: would I be able to find enough water to insure my sugar balance?

CHAPTER **3**

Equipment

I SOON REALIZED that it was not going to be too difficult, statistics in hand, to convince the scientists, but winning over the sailors was a different matter. As soon as I broached the object of my experiments their invariable reply was: "That's all very well in theory. It may make sense shut up in a laboratory, but it will be quite another thing at sea, you take my word for it."

There was still one overwhelming factor to be taken into consideration: how to defeat the greatest killer of them all, despair. It formed no part of the study of nutrition, but if drink is more important than food, instilling confidence is more important than drink. Thirst kills more quickly than hunger, but despair is a greater danger than thirst. "What I will is fate," as Milton wrote. I had to take into account the whole question of morale.

Who is most likely to suffer disaster at sea? The scientist, the sailor, the doctor, or the fisherman? In this sphere, medical science seemed to stop at the arid teachings of the physiologist. It was up to me to obtain practical evidence. If my theory was to be something more than a hypothesis, if it was to serve some real purpose, it was essential to reduce the experiment to human terms in an actual sea voyage. I had to find some way of isolating myself on the ocean for a period of between one and three months. The route I chose must have favorable winds and currents, but be unfrequented, to relieve us of the temptation of boarding any of the ships we met. Only by some such exploit could we fire imaginations with the proof that life can be sustained far from land.

I started to read accounts of freak voyages, particularly by those who had sailed alone. Undoubtedly the best work on the subject is that of my friend Jean Merrien, *Les Navigateurs Solitaires.* I won't go into detail about it here, but it makes two things clear: to attract attention it would be necessary for me to cross one of the great oceans, preferably the Atlantic; and if a voyage was to last two months without there being too much temptation to abandon it, it would be best to follow the northeast trade wind and follow two of the routes made by Christopher Columbus from Spain, via the Canaries, past the Cape Verde Islands to the West Indies. This would avoid the main trade routes, which pass to the north for North America and the West Indies, and to the south for South America. It would also pass between the Sargasso Sea and the Doldrums, where we would risk certain disaster without benefit to anyone.

Life at Monaco was extremely busy. I spent whole days in the library examining the index cards file by file and extracting, with the help of M. Comet, the librarian, my supply of books for the week. Almost every day I went out in one of the boats belonging to the Museum, the *Pisa* or the *Eider,* and pressed every conceivable variety of fish in an attempt to obtain the maximum quantity of liquid, paying particular attention to the taste. I also discovered that the best possible instrument for doing this was a simple fruit press.

Gradually I accustomed myself to the diet I had devised and became more confident as the results proved satisfactory. In the laboratory at least, it seemed that my theory was completely sound. By a miracle, I had managed to keep my project more or less

secret, although in this I may have been helped by the polite disbelief and benevolent incredulity of those who knew about it. To tell the truth, I was probably the only person who really believed in what I was doing.

Little by little, the tentative date we had fixed for our departure was put forward. Originally there were to be three of us, van Hemsbergen, our sponsor, and myself. Then we became five and, finally, six. At one point we had decided to use a ship's lifeboat. Then our sponsor turned to a really extraordinary craft.

He suddenly made up his mind to use a sort of Polynesian catamaran consisting of two hulls supporting a deck and a sail—really only suitable for use in a sheltered bay. He sent one down to us with the suggestion that we try to get to Corsica and back in it. Our experience with this glorified water scooter had a lot to do with my finally making the voyage alone.

Van Hemsbergen and I spent several days playing around with this ridiculous craft in the harbor, to the intense amusement of the onlookers, and then had it towed out to sea one fine morning toward the end of November. A slight breeze sprang up about eleven o'clock and the catamaran fairly scudded over the waves. We had turned for home when one of the leeboards broke. It should be explained that the two hulls were open and it was possible to sit in them rather like a canoe. We had made no attempt to cover them, even though they shipped quite a lot of water, as we wanted to test the craft's stability. With the head no longer able to keep into the sea, the inevitable soon happened. A wave broke into one of the pontoons and the whole thing turned turtle. We were well out into the bay of Monte Carlo and the wind was carrying us toward Cape Martin. We both managed to reach the shore. I swam and Jean was picked up by a launch. The police even got mixed up in the affair. I had scraped my thigh on the sharp rocks, and they received a report that a naked, bleeding man had been seen staggering around in the woods. It was clear that I was not going to become a voluntary castaway without a few preliminary involuntary experiences.

This episode should have been enough to prove to our sponsor the futility of this particular line of investigation. But, on the contrary, he drew up ambitious plans for a large catamaran nearly fifty feet long with a cabin and a galley! It was clear that we were developing different conceptions of both ends and means. Whenever I ventured a few mild suggestions and protests, I was told that it was essential to give the expedition an international character, that several types of boat would probably take part, that there was still plenty of time, and that he even had plans for us to sail around the world. The whole project became increasingly visionary until it seemed that we had completely lost sight of the basic problem of the castaway.

In my own mind I slowly built up an obstinate resolution to stick to our original plans, to work only with this object in view, and then present my colleagues with a *fait accompli*. I was sure that once everything was ready, vacillating minds would be made up and the expedition would really revert to its initial purpose. I was told that everything would be ready for about May or June, so I decided to make my own plans accordingly. Then we would start, with the blessing, I was certain, of our patron.

By the end of March my theoretical work was, to all intents and purposes, finished. My next-door neighbor in the laboratory was Dr. S. K. Kon, of Reading University, who had come to Monaco to study the family of the minute planktonic crustaceans, the principal food of whales, which are to be found at the surface of the sea between Mentone and Cape Martin. Dr. Kon suggested that I should meet one or two experts who would be able to complete my information. I therefore paid a quick visit to England, where, thanks to him and to Dr. Magee, of the Ministry of Health, I was put in touch with representatives of the navy and air force, of whom one, Dr. Wittingham, became my good friend. They were all greatly interested in my projects and expressed doubts when they had any. Dr. Wittingham also met our patron and paid us a short visit in Monaco. My only regret was that on two occasions I missed meeting Professor MacCance, the Cambridge plankton specialist.

My journey was not without its curious repercussions. Passing through the Customs at Calais, one of the inspectors said to me:

"Another Channel crossing, eh?"

I smiled and replied: "Oh, no, this time it's the Atlantic."

He gave a short, incredulous laugh, but on reflection must have said to himself: "After all why not? . . ." and passed on the tip to a British newspaper.

Thus it was that the press started to take an interest in us. One day a journalist came to interview me at the laboratory in Monaco and a whole sequence of reports began to appear, many of them grossly distorting the facts. Without realizing it, I had started a chain of events beside which the adventures of the sorcerer's apprentice pale into insignificance. The reports became increasingly grotesque. I was referred to as "Professor" Bombard with all sorts of academic titles. . . . It all acquired the tone of the worst form of publicity campaign and seriously interfered with my work. The only good result was the stream of volunteers who offered their services. There was no danger of my lacking company. Still counting on van Hemsbergen, I only needed one more member to complete the crew. One day a tall Englishman, sandy-haired, of the true phlegmatic type, came to place himself, his sextant, and his boat at my disposal. His name was Herbert Muir-Palmer, a naturalized citizen of Panama, better known as Jack Palmer. A first-class seaman and navigator, he had sailed from Panama across the Atlantic and through the Mediterranean to Cairo; and then, in company with his wife, from Cairo back to Monaco, with a little ten-meter yacht, the *Hermione*, touching at Cyprus, Tobruk, and passing through the Straits of Messina. He had been at Monaco for a year or so, short of money, like so many of these solitary sailors. I told him all about our plans: how two or three

of us wanted to place ourselves in the situation of shipwrecked survivors in a lifeboat or life raft, without food or water, in order to
prove to the world that survival was possible under such conditions. He asked me to give him a few hours to think it over,
not wanting to commit himself lightly. Then he came back and
said:

"Dr. Bombard, I am your man."

He turned out to be more delightful every day and I was over-
joyed with our "find." But we were still safely on land. In spite
of myself I could not help thinking: What will he be like when we
get really hungry? What happens if we fall out between ourselves?
I know Hemsbergen's reactions, but what about Palmer's?

It was with this thought in mind that we finally decided to make
a trial run in the Mediterranean instead of setting off straightaway
from Tangier or Casablanca. This almost landlocked sea, so de-
ceptively like a lake, would test both men and equipment. The
worse it behaved the greater service it would render. We would
know all the difficulties confronting us and would then be able
to challenge the Atlantic.

As I have said, the people who had made the *Hitchhiker* were
constructing a similar craft, somewhat larger. It seemed as though
the discussions would never end. In the meantime I continued
to receive countless offers from volunteers and had to put up with
a swarm of newspapermen. Some of the letters I received were
quaint in the extreme. One prospective crew member tried to
strengthen his case by offering to allow himself to be eaten if
the experiment failed. Another wrote to say that he had already
tried to commit suicide three times and asked to be allowed to
accompany us as it seemed a suitable method of renewing his
attempts. Yet a third proposed that I should take his mother-in-law
as a passenger, suggesting that my efforts of lifesaving could well
start by rescuing a marriage which was being wrecked by the
person in question. Another correspondent asked how he could
keep flowers alive with sea water, since I claimed it had no

deleterious effects. Of course, there were other genuine offers of experimental equipment for testing purposes.

On May 15, a Thursday, I received a telephone call from Jean-Luc de Carbuccia, who had become my close friend, offering a contract to publish the book I was planning to write about my experiences. This made the expedition more or less self-sufficient, since it would leave my wife without material worries. Two days later I went to Paris and, after a final heated argument with the manufacturer, took over the craft which was to become *L'Hérétique*. Triumphant, I returned to Monaco with my personal transatlantic liner. At long last the expedition was about to start. I sent telegrams to van Hemsbergen and our patron, who arrived the evening before we were due to set off, saying: "This is the best day of my life, not only my birthday, but the start of the adventure. Van Hemsbergen has been detained, but I have come to take his place."

I then had to convince him that his three hundred and fifty pounds could not possibly be accommodated in such a frail vessel and that it would be a much greater service to the expedition if he would stay behind and organize the next stage. Palmer and I were ready to leave the following day, the twenty-fourth. The designer of our boat, the well-known airman Debroutelle, was attending to the last details of our inflatable dinghy in the harbor of Monaco.

It was a sort of horseshoe-shaped inflatable rubber sausage, fifteen feet long and six feet wide, and seemed the perfect piece of equipment for such an expedition as ours. The open end was closed by a wooden sternboard, over which we were to be able to trail our fishing nets and lines without causing damage by friction to the fragile rubber floats. The bottom of the boat was about three feet wide and supported a lightweight wooden deck board.

There was not a single piece of metal in the whole construction. The floats were divided into five compartments—the curved bow and two along each side—by hermetically sealed rubber bulkheads. An outside valve, which could be turned on and off as required, allowed air to pass from one compartment to the other. It will be seen in due course how useful this arrangement was. The deck, or bottom—it was one and the same—was practically flat, and there was a rigid keel running the length of the boat. It had a dinghy sail of about three square yards, but the mast was placed too far forward, which made it impossible to sail into the wind. However, there were two leeboards fixed about a third of the way down the sides. These gave the craft a certain degree of maneuverability, although actually we were to use them only when approaching land.

All I needed now was a sailing permit, a simple enough formality, one would have thought. In this case it turned out to be extremely difficult. At one moment it looked as if the whole project would collapse for the lack of this one piece of paper. A few days earlier I had learned that the local court in the north of France had ruled in my absence that I should pay a suspended fine of two thousand francs for breaking the regulations concerning navigation on the high seas. Wishing to defend myself, I jumped into a train to go and protest the verdict.

The second act of what I have called the Comic Interlude took place in the imposing surroundings of a court of petty sessions. I was charged with having used on the high seas, without a navigation permit, a craft designed only for use off the beach.

My turn came to speak:

"Your Honor, I must say I find it strange that I'm the only one called on this charge. I was merely a passenger in a boat whose owner was on board. I should also like to ask whether I would have been granted a navigation permit if I had asked for it?"

"It would neither have been refused nor granted, and is not pertinent to this case."

At this point the prosecutor, who had not said a word up till then, jumped up like a jack-in-the-box and launched into a violent diatribe:

"Your Honor," he said, "the Court should know that the accused is a public danger, whose bad example might well cause loss of life among the young people in these parts. He has already been fined two thousand francs in default. As he has committed two offenses, there should be a double fine."

"Sir, I am in process of conducting an experiment of possible world-wide importance," I tried to explain. "In the interests of all concerned I hope you will not find it necessary to fine me."

The prosecutor broke in again: "It is quite clear that the accused is an irresponsible hoaxer," he said. "This experiment only exists in his own imagination."

After due deliberation, the Court imposed two suspended fines of a thousand francs each. There was no time to enter an appeal, so I returned to Monaco.

On my return, I received another visitor, whose machinations were to imperil the whole expedition. He was a good-looking reporter in his early thirties, with all the energy and vulgarity of a certain type of journalist. No sooner had he started to interview me when he said:

"Do you have a radio transmitter?"

"No."

"Well, you're in luck because I am going to see that you get one."

I looked at my benefactor open-mouthed, hardly able to believe in this unexpected offer. Then he went on:

"We are very much interested in your experiment. However, you must realize that putting a radio transmitter-receiver in a craft such as yours presents a number of technical problems. We would like to go into them with you. Is this agreeable to you?"

I shook hands with him effusively.

"It may take time to get a broadcasting license from the Principality, but let us know as soon as you get it and we'll bring the equipment immediately."

"You do realize," I said, "that I would then need the set as quickly as possible because it will take time to install it."

"Leave it to us," he answered, and off he went.

Delighted with this new development, I put in the necessary application to the Monaco administration, with a request that it should be given priority. I received the license on May 23. However, since I had been given advance notice of its arrival, I was able to pass the word to the reporter on May 20.

While in Paris, on May 16, I had told Jean-Luc all about this offer. Instead of becoming as excited as I was, he was slightly discouraging.

"Have you any idea of the complications involved?" he asked. "It would need a professional expert or at least a highly gifted amateur to maintain contact with such a tiny set across two thousand miles of ocean."

This I did not doubt, as I had already tried to impress on my reporter friend that I was a complete novice when it came to radios.

"All the more reason for your having one," he had said.

Jean-Luc, not sharing my confidence, thought over the problem, and after I had left Paris got in touch with a friend of his named Jean Ferré, who was connected with the French Broadcasting System. I wasn't a bit worried. I had yet to learn that I was not going to get a radio, but that by way of compensation I would gain two good friends.

On May 22 Jean Ferré telephoned me from Paris. His curiosity was only equaled by his indignation: "What sort of valves do you have?" he asked me. "What type of aerial? What is your source of power? What wave lengths will you work on? What is the make of the receiver?"

"I have complete confidence in the people who are giving me the equipment," I stammered in reply.

"But experts would expect to take months to study this problem," he went on. "Radio amateurs like me with modest equipment and not operating under the best of conditions need at least two weeks to put them in full working order even when the sets are already installed. Today is the twenty-second and you want to leave on the twenty-fourth without as much as having seen your equipment yet. You must be crazy. . . ." And he hung up.

Thoroughly shaken, I rang up my journalist friend: "Please hurry up. I am leaving on the twenty-fourth," I said.

"We know that perfectly well, dear Doctor Bombard, just have confidence in us," he replied.

On the morning of the twenty-third I went to meet Carbuccia and Ferré at the station. Ferré was brandishing a typed document:

"The President of the French Broadcasting System has the honor to present to Doctor Bombard Monsieur Jean Ferré F 9 O V, with a view to studying the technical problems involved in maintaining a radio link during his voyage. M. Ferré will inform Doctor Bombard of the steps that have been taken to co-operate with this sporting and scientific experiment of such interest to radio amateurs.

"Signed: Marcheville F 8 N H."

Perhaps it should be pointed out that every amateur transmitter is allotted a call sign by the French postal administration. In France these signs begin with an F, while those of Monte Carlo commence with 3 A 9.

I was astonished at the official turn things had taken. It was then explained to me that I had become a special case. Since what I was going to do had never been attempted before, special provisions would have to be made for the equipment I needed. First of all, it would have to be hermetically sealed against sea water and condensation and must not be too heavy for the boat. It would need an absolutely foolproof source of power and must be capable of working with any type of aerial and on a variety of wave lengths. It would need either a very experienced operator or a highly complicated set of controls.

Jean Ferré spared me no details: "Working on short waves is a tricky business. You might need to work between ten and forty meters in order to insure contact. In certain conditions even a one-hundred-kilowatt transmitter cannot be heard, and yours will only have the strength of ten watts."

There was only one solution, he told me, and that was to enlist the assistance of the radio "hams." There are more than two hundred thousand of them scattered around the globe, with long experience in picking up feeble signals. The French Broadcasting

System would send them a notice about me and there would always be someone on watch day and night. I could only stutter my thanks at the thought of this immense host of well-wishers who would be on the lookout for me.

"For them to be able to pick you up at all I must first have a good look at your equipment," Jean Ferré said. There was still no sign of it or its donors. Jean Ferré rang them up himself. "Do not worry, the stuff is on its way," he was told.

"Have you any idea of the problems facing you?"

"Yes, of course."

"What sort of aerial have you in mind?"

"We are going to fix it on the mast."

"The mast of the dinghy is not more than six feet high. An aerial there would have no range at all."

There was silence from the other end.

"Why don't you use a balloon or a kite?" Jean Ferré suggested.

"Good idea."

"What make is the receiver?"

"Everything is in hand."

"What frequency are you using?"

"Thirty megacycles."

We sent off this information by telegram to M. de Marcheville. His reply came back immediately: "Thirty m/c frequency of W W V. Do not understand."

We did not understand either. W W V is the station of the National Bureau of Standards in Washington, which floods the ether with its one-hundred-kilowatt transmitter. Quite clearly my own little set was not going to be able to compete with it on the same wave length.

We telephoned my benefactors again.

"Don't worry, everything will be all right," they insisted.

That evening, Friday the twenty-third, one of their representatives arrived in Monaco. "I have come to prepare the ground," he said. "The equipment will arrive tomorrow."

We told him all about the problems involved. He seemed astonished at our doubts.

"The whole thing is quite simple," he said.

As for me, I was now convinced that the radio idea was hopeless. I thought of telephoning to say that I would leave without it and that they should call the whole thing off. But even then I hesitated. Perhaps they had thought out all the problems, and who was I to nullify their efforts.

My wife was getting anxious too. "Do you think we are going to be able to keep in touch with Alain?" she asked Jean Ferré. He did not reply. He was pacing up and down like a lion in a cage thinking of the hundreds of hours needed to adjust an amateur's transmitter and of all the experts a commercial company would have employed for the job. And here we were without as much as a piece of wire.

We had decided to sail on the twenty-fourth at three o'clock in the afternoon. At eleven o'clock in the morning a group of people arrived with the equipment, my reporter friend among them. He buttonholed Jean Ferré: "Who do I negotiate with for exclusive rights?" he asked.

Jean looked at him with blank incomprehension. "Exclusive rights? What exclusive rights? I thought your whole idea was simply to help two people who are risking their lives on behalf of shipwrecked mariners?"

"The exclusive broadcasting rights. You understand, of course, that I can sell them to the B.B.C., perhaps even to the Americans, if I have the rights."

While this was going on I was looking at the set. The transmitter was a simple chassis without any protective covering, such as one might install with infinite precautions on a laboratory table. The receiver was a simple commercial battery model. Only the generator was a piece of quality equipment.

"What about the aerial?" I asked.

"The best we have been able to manage in the time is a kite," I was told.

At midday Jean Ferré called a meeting in my room at the hotel. "On behalf of the French Broadcasting System, which has asked me to give my opinion in this matter, I must state without equivocation that there is no possibility of maintaining contact between the dinghy and land with this equipment," he said. "First of all the sets are not protected against sea water. It would take an expert to use them. The first shock or the loss of the aerial would mean complete breakdown. Everyone would think the expedition had been lost at sea, and this would only cause unnecessary anxiety. Neither Bombard nor Palmer have any knowledge of Morse and there is no means of voice transmission."

"Doctor Bombard," the others replied, "you have nothing to worry about. This gentleman here no doubt means well but he lacks experience. Have confidence in us, we will keep watch for your messages."

My friends were appalled and my wife consumed with worry. I held a council of war with Palmer. I knew the radio would never work, but after all what did it matter. A month earlier I had not even dreamed of having one. In any case, a castaway would be unlikely to be equipped with a radio transmitter. We decided to start just the same. However, since the wind was in the wrong quarter and we put off our departure for twenty-four hours, the interim was used to install the set.

I shall never forget the last sentence of the radio commentator describing the scene from the launch which towed us out to sea on Sunday the twenty-fifth. "We will ask your news in the form of questions. Please signal a dot for yes and a dash for no. Good-by, Doctor. Remember dot yes, dash no, dot yes, dash no. . . ."

But I really must put on record the events of the day that preceded our departure. Once the press had started to interest itself in our expedition, we had been increasingly hounded by journalists and curiosity seekers. There's now nothing for me to learn about the art of the news photographer trying to find the best angle for a shot. My work had been hampered for weeks. I always seemed to have a newspaperman at my elbow. The twenty-four hours before our departure became a circus. I could not even walk along the street with my wife without being tapped on the shoulder by some complete stranger who asked me to stand there and kiss her so that he could get a good photograph.

This wave of publicity placed our expedition in the worst possible light. Certainly the press has a right to keep the public informed. I realize that quite often it is not so much a sober account of the facts as the human angle which interests the great mass of readers. But the whole spirit of the expedition was falsified in the eyes of a number of people and discredited in the minds of others. The circumstances were sensationalized to the point of completely losing sight of the reasons for our preliminary lap in the Mediterranean, namely that of testing equipment and crew. The trouble was that the least contradiction in practice to the results we expected in theory to attain, or what we were maneuvered into saying we hoped to attain, would be more than sufficient to discredit the whole enterprise. No attempt was made to appreciate that we had everything to learn and that we still had to work out the minute day-to-day routine on board. We were presented as the stars of a drama. As I have said, we never intended the Mediterranean to be more than a dress rehearsal, but now our slightest failure would be held against us. The completely false situation drummed up by the press was particularly dangerous in view of the fact that we were setting out to challenge generally accepted principles and the dictates of common sense.

I was a heretic on several counts. We were going to try and reach, in a craft not considered capable of navigation, a destination determined in advance. This first heresy particularly aroused the professional seamen and navigators who assured us that we would never get farther than the Iles d'Hyères. Furthermore, I was attacking the general belief that it was impossible to live on the resources of the sea alone and that sea water was undrinkable. Moreover, to paraphrase the comments made in one of the more reputable publications: although experienced seamen never felt absolutely confident of their ability to cope with the dangers of sea, winds, and currents, here was a rank amateur who did not hesitate to trust his companion's life and his own to a ridiculous cockleshell whose design had not even been approved by a qualified maritime specialist.

For these reasons, and many others, I named our ship *L'Hérétique*.

Fortunately, we still enjoyed the support of one or two persons in authority. Due to the personal intervention of the Undersecretary of State at the Navy Ministry, M. Jacques Gavini, I was granted my navigation permit. Thus it was that *L'Hérétique* was able to fly the French flag all the way across the Atlantic.

PART TWO

MEDITERRANEAN

CHAPTER **4**

Departure

WE ALL MET at dawn in the little harbor of Fonvieille. Harassed by importunate newspapermen, to whose questions I replied to the best of my ability, I supervised the loading of equipment into the dinghy. A large crowd had started to gather, even though we had no intention of setting off until about three o'clock in the afternoon, when wind conditions were normally at their best. The group of electricians worked away feverishly to put the wireless transmitter in order, accompanied by a constant round of advice by the local amateurs from Monte Carlo and Nice. About two o'clock an official arrived to seal the jerry cans of emergency water we were carrying in case the experiment ended in disaster. Then a messenger from the Museum of Oceanography came to tell me that the Museum's boat was not available to tow us out to sea on a Saturday or Sunday.

This point should be explained. The dinghy was incapable of sailing into the wind. In order to become castaways, we had to start as far away from the coast as possible, as otherwise an unfavorable wind would have driven us straight back again. It was therefore necessary, as with the Kon-Tiki, for us to be towed out about a dozen miles off the coast. Fortunately, there was an

41

American cruiser anchored in the bay, whose captain agreed to lend us one of his launches for the purpose.

By this time, the crowd was immense. The spectators were clearly tired of waiting and were impatient to see us leave. Unfortunately, the wind had veered to the southwest and was almost certain to drive us ashore if we set off. Since the captain of the American cruiser agreed to lend us the launch again the next morning, we decided to put off our departure till then. Jack seemed to think that the wind would veer in our favor, a prognostication confirmed by the local meteorological station, which, for once, got its forecast right. As soon as the crowd learned of our decision, there were loud cries of complaint. A big fellow came up to me, dressed in sort of cowboy style, with a wide hat, and gave me this piece of advice:

"Young man, I know something about this business, I have just returned from South America. There is no point in being squeamish. If your companion dies on the way, don't throw him overboard. Eat him. Anything serves as food, I have even eaten shark."

"Thank you," I replied politely. "I will follow your advice."

Then I went back to the hotel to get some rest.

We were back again in the harbor about half-past four in the morning. The crowd had reduced itself to our own friends. The atmosphere was completely different; everything had suddenly become real. We were no longer a circus act, but two people leaving on a long and arduous voyage. I suddenly felt buoyed up; we were really off. Ginette, my wife, was there, Jean Ferré, Jean-Luc de Carbuccia, a few reporters, together with the technicians. Jack and I ordered a last cup of coffee and a ham roll. By the time they were brought, we had changed our minds and we refused to eat them. After all, we thought, whether we stopped eating then or a few hours later was immaterial. We had no idea how much we were to regret our quixotic gesture during the long days of fast we were to endure.

Five o'clock. With true naval punctuality, the American cruiser's launch swept into the little harbor. In spite of the early hour, the captain himself had come along to direct operations. Everything was ready. Jack and I climbed silently into *L'Hérétique* with lumps in our throats. We had barely exchanged a couple of words the whole morning.

"Ready?" shouted the captain.

"Yes."

"Let's go."

Slowly the launch took up the tow and made for the open sea. We sat opposite each other on the inflated floats, our legs dangling inboard. The sea was quite choppy, giving us a foretaste of what bad weather was going to be like. The waves seemed short and unpredictable, running irregularly and breaking continuously. The launch rolled and pitched, but the dinghy, in spite of the sea, remained remarkably steady, which seemed a good omen. It rode the waves well, with very little motion. Everyone in the launch was hunched over and hanging on to something to keep on their feet, and every now and again the clapper of its bell swung with the swell and gave out a sharp peal. With our hands completely free, Jack and I waved good-by to those left on shore. Right from the start, we felt, *L'Hérétique* was proving superior to orthodox vessels.

Ginette was in the launch, making brave efforts to smile, but her dark sunglasses hid the tears I knew were in her eyes. A few hundred yards out we were joined by two or three other craft and our departure took on the appearance of a regatta.

Although we responded to their smiles and waved back at them, Jack and I already had the sensation that we were well on our way and no longer belonged to their world. We were already becoming part of our frail craft, the only home we were to know for many a long day and the center of our universe. The sea was covered with white horses, soon to become familiar companions.

As their spray started to soak us, the launch sounded its bell. At a sign from Jack the tow was dropped.

We waved and shouted our good-bys. The accompanying craft circled round us a couple of times and we responded mechanically to their parting gestures. Although they did not realize it, our fellow human beings had become strangers. We had a sudden feeling that we had parted company with mankind. Our new life at sea had become more real and tangible than our relationships with those still so close. "Off with you then," would have been the only words with meaning that we could have shouted, but although we may have thought this, we remained silent.

Slowly the other boats disappeared from view. Soon we were completely alone, isolated in a strange new element in the cockle-shell which was our only support. Fear, the enemy which was to attack me so often during the coming seven months, laid its clammy hand on me for the first time. The sensation only lasted a brief moment, compared with the deep wounds it had yet to cause me. We were to know the feeling well, not this light touch of fear at the moment of departure, but the panic revolt of body and soul terrified by the elements, as if the whole universe had become one dreadful menace.

The wind started to blow in strong gusts, and spray hid the still sleeping land. We could just see the top of the "Tête de Chien" and the Italian cliffs by Bordighera. All that remained of the boats which had brought us out were their white wakes on the horizon. We were face to face with the unknown. We had conjured up visions of this solitude for so long that it seemed like some strange gift one had dreamed about for years suddenly being presented in tangible form. The sea and the wind we knew, and the sound of the waves, but this was our first true rendezvous with them. Now that we were there, everything seemed to fall into place and all was well.

Jack and I sat in oppressive silence. It seemed as if the whole future were weighing down on us. We did not hoist the sail im-

mediately, as Jack was afraid it might tear in the strong wind and
he wanted to test its strength and that of the mast by degrees. In
order not to be driven back to Nice, we used, for the first time,
our floating sea anchor. This was a device much in favor in sailing days, and revived for modern use by the famous Captain
Voss. It can consist of any half-submerged object strung from
the bow on a length of rope. Its purpose is to keep the head of a
ship into the wind in order to meet the waves in the most favorable
position. In a storm, all the sails are taken in and the ship drifts
before the wind, with the sea anchor acting as a brake. This prevents the boat's turning beam onto the wind and possibly cap-
sizing. Our sea anchor consisted of a little parachute which filled
under the pressure of water, thus slowing down our progress. Later
on, in order to support my theories, which demanded the minimum
amount of equipment on board, I used my sea anchor for other
purposes as well, such as catching plankton.

With this anchor out, *L'Hérétique* turned docilely to face the
Italian coast. The sun rose slowly, dissipating the mist, and re-
vealed the dangerous coast looming nearer than we had expected.
We had to get as much sea room as possible in order to pass the
various points and promontories which stuck out like traps along
our route. The most important of these were Cape Ferrat, Cape

d'Antibes and the Lérins Islands, followed by Cape Camarat and the island of Levant, which our more pessimistic friends had told us we would never succeed in passing. After that the coast turned north and west and we had open sea in front of us.

The wind died down somewhat and we hoisted our sail. This was a complicated operation as the mast was in the fore part of the boat. We had covered the forward part of the bathtub-shaped dinghy with a tent, leaving the afterpart as an open deck about six feet long and three feet, six inches wide. Since we could not walk across the tent to reach the bow, as we would have gone right through the thin fabric, we had to perform a fantastic tight-rope act along the floats. The return journey was even more acrobatic as there was not even a mast to make for. I usually laid out flat, pulling myself along by my arms.

L'Hérétique started to pick up speed. I must say it made a splendid sight, sailing large with the main sheet paid right out, leaving a broad wake which bore no relation to our speed, although there was a fine sensation of forward motion. We set up a considerable backwash, the height of which we hoped would give us some indication of our speed. Later I was to judge this more accurately by the pull of the sail on the main sheet. For the time being we were probably not making more than a knot and a half, but that was better than nothing.

About eleven o'clock, just as we were rounding Cape Ferrat, the wind died down suddenly. Apparently it was by no means easy to become a voluntary castaway. We had still hardly spoken a word and it required an effort to break the silence. Each of us was thinking of what we had left behind. However, it did not take us long to react normally to events. All our memories and regrets as landsmen reasserted themselves. The loved ones we had abandoned soon reoccupied their accustomed places in our minds. The mood of feeling like legendary heroes passed and we became normal people again.

To pull ourselves together, we held our first council of war, each one making an effort to appear calm and collected in the eyes of the other. The most difficult thing was to talk in a normal tone of voice, as we both had a tendency to mutter. This was significant. We realized that if we continued to murmur like this, the specter of fear would take it as an invitation to assert itself.

Taking advantage of this uneventful interval, we started to work out the details of our life on board. We put out a couple of fishing lines as a step toward the next meal and then set about planning every minute of the day in much more detail than during the long period of preparation on land. The first problem was to organize the watches. Each of us was to take turns at the tiller during the day, while the other rested, as I was certain that the abnormal life we were about to lead would demand the maximum amount of sleep. What we could not finally settle was how to divide up the night. In a sea as traveled as the Mediterranean, it was essential for one of us to be on watch, so we decided that one of us would take over from eight in the evening until one in the morning, and the other from then until eight in the morning.

Everything on board was stowed where we could find it immediately even in pitch darkness. In the bow, under the tent, protected from sea and damp in watertight containers we put the cameras, films, navigation books, the sextant, first-aid box, the stock of flares for use in an emergency, the sealed boxes of food, and the repair kit. The compass was in its binnacle, just in front of the steersman, so that he could keep his eye on it at all times.

No fish had nibbled at the hooks by lunchtime, but during the morning we had replaced the sea anchor by the plankton net, which not only rendered the same service, but collected a supply of food, sufficient as to composition if not in quantity. In about an hour the net caught two full tablespoons of a sort of pap by no means unpleasant to the taste and quite filling, despite not being particularly appetizing to look at. For the greater part it consisted of animal plankton, almost exclusively copepods, with a flavor like crab or lobster purée; really quite a feast. Jack watched me eat my share with a somewhat doubtful look. Not wanting to appear timid, he finally took a taste. To his surprise he found the dish by no means unpleasant and I discreetly enjoyed my first victory.

We had both become much calmer and, as this superb late spring day progressed, our presence in this heretical craft suddenly appeared quite normal. All our anxieties disappeared. This gradual normalization, the calm after the storm, this quick healing of psychological wounds, was to become the regular pattern in the Atlantic, to the point where there seemed nothing out of the ordinary in the strange life I was leading. My theories were already finding their justification. It was just a question of getting the first few hours of adaptation behind me.

It has been maintained that sea water is laxative. It may be that the sulphates of calcium and magnesium it contains have this effect on land, when other factors are normal, but after my experiences, I assert emphatically that this is not the case at sea, a fact which certain German experiments have confirmed. Jack was much more hesitant to give it a trial and preferred to await a catch of fish or a rainstorm before slaking his thirst. In spite of my advice and arguments he refused to take a drop. It was a striking example of the danger caused by habits too deeply rooted, but he was not to be moved even when I drank a glass myself.

While still on land he had agreed completely with my theory and fully intended to make the experiment, but once faced by reality, the taboo of so many generations blocked his previous intentions. So there we were, literally in the same boat, one of us conforming to the inhibitions of the classic castaway and the other with his heretical ideas. Suddenly Jack's voice broke into my thoughts:

"Alain, it is three o'clock and they will be expecting our first radio message. We might as well take advantage of the calm."

I agreed, but we had few illusions about its efficiency, most of them having been destroyed by Jean Ferré before our departure. We knew that our jerry-built set was a laboratory instrument liable to damage at the least shock, that its wiring and circuits were entirely at the mercy of dampness. We were convinced that the thing was not going to work, but, there, it was three o'clock. . . . For several minutes now all around the Mediterranean, radio amateurs would be searching the air waves, ignorant of the inadequacy of our equipment.

"It's three o'clock," Jack repeated.

I thought of my wife, alone in Monaco, of Radio Geneva, and of the jerry can of water we had had to leave behind to compensate for the weight of the set. I thought of all the telephone calls my wife would be receiving about four o'clock to say: "We have been listening for them over an hour." Perhaps, after all, Jean Ferré was wrong. Perhaps it was true that the set had been constructed especially for our purposes. Perhaps we were going to be able to maintain contact with land. My hopes rose. Perhaps this combination of wires and valves served some purpose after all. Surely no one would deliberately take advantage of two men engaged in such an adventure as ours.

"Jack, let's get the aerial up," I said.

The aerial. Have you ever tried to launch a kite without moving from your chair? The experts had either overlooked this problem or had assumed that we could. I hope that someday I can persuade one of them to try and launch a kite with its precious aerial as we had to from a platform six feet long. We must have cut a ridiculous figure, lurching and stumbling with each wave. And then the kite plunged into the sea, soaked and useless. We were overcome by a sense of horror.

"Put up the emergency aerial," I cried. This was a steel fishing rod on a halyard. Our mast was about fifteen feet high, apparently not much higher than the waves, and the wire which led down from it was attached to the transmitter. I tried the pilot light, tapped the amperemeter, and said to Jack: "Turn the thing."

The generator between his knees started to make a grinding

noise, and a mysterious current seemed to run through everything. The valves lit up. Rather like firing my last shot, I started tapping the Morse key. . . . I must have repeated the message a hundred times. I turned all the knobs, tested all the wires, put my fingers on the contacts to see if there was any sign of the expected two hundred and fifty volts. Nothing happened. A single drop of water or some slight shock to the quartz crystal had been enough. . . .

Without my saying a word, Jack stopped turning the generator; his gaze met mine. "It's no good," I said. "Now we are completely alone. . . ."

Night fell in a multicolored sky and the first lighthouse appeared on our right: that of Cape d'Antibes, which we recognized from the description in our *Pilot Book*. This is a volume, published by the naval authorities, which gives the characteristics, by areas, of every lighthouse in existence. Each is different according to the duration and frequency of the flash, its color, and grouping, and all are perfectly easy to identify.

Then the night breeze sprang up from the land and carried us out to sea. It was a factor we had not taken into account. Those who were convinced that a dozen hours would find us thrown back on some beach were proved mistaken. We had scored a decisive point which, by its very nature, gave us encouragement from the first day. Perhaps, after all, we should have been grateful to the doubters, as otherwise the triumph would not have seemed as sweet.

The first night was upon us. I had drawn the first watch until one in the morning and we were to reverse the order the next day. This arrangement soon proved indispensable, as the first watch from eight o'clock until one proved much more tiring than the second in spite of its greater length.

During the day we assumed various positions, not all of them particularly safe, but we settled down for the night with the steersman sitting next to the rudder oar, with his back resting on a Mae

West, and the compass between his legs, a deliberately uncomfortable position which prevented him from dropping off to sleep.
His feet touched the end of the tent, which protected the sleeping
partner. To make enough room for the man off watch to stretch
out, we had ranged all the equipment along the left-hand side of
our "bathtub," leaving a space about two feet wide and nearly six
feet long. The tent served as a blanket and the bags as a pillow.

Jack dropped off to sleep, but I was not the only one awake. At
nightfall the sea became a hive of activity. All its inhabitants apparently came to take a look at us, and the snorts of porpoises and
splashes of leaping fish around the boat peopled the night with
strange phantoms, formidable at first, but soon familiar. The slap
of the waves resolved itself into a regular murmur punctuated
by occasional noises, like the voice of a soloist against a muted
orchestra. *"La mer, la mer toujours recommencée, s'exprimant
dans un tumulte au silence pareil."* * That expresses it perfectly.
The regular movement of the sea ends by seeming as silent as the
summit of a high mountain. Silence and noise are always relative,
like the miller who only woke up when his millstone stopped turning. Silence can be as expressive as any sound. Does not Bach, that
master of an orchestra, make superb use of an interval of silence in
his D-minor Toccata? An organ point floating on silence.

The land breeze lasted the whole of the night. Before getting
into the region of regular winds, we were relying largely on the
alternation of sea and land breezes to make progress. The breeze
blows off the sea during the morning and then pauses as if to draw
breath, to be followed by the breeze off the land in the evening,
as if to bring a fresh supply of air for the night. It was as if the
ocean heaved a great sigh every day, carrying along our frail craft
in its great torrent of breath.

The phenomenon has, of course, a perfectly rational explanation, familiar to every schoolchild: during the morning while the
sun rises, the land warms up more quickly than the sea, and the

* P. Valéry, *Le Cimitière marin.*

air above it rises. The colder sea air moves in to take its place, thereby forming a circuit of movement. But just as the sea warms more slowly, it retains its heat longer, and during the night the air movement is reversed as the land cools off. What we had to do was to take advantage of the night wind and lay up during the day.

The first night showed how essential it was to keep watch. We met at least ten ships. Low in the water, our riding light was practically invisible and certainly insufficient to insure our safety. To meet this danger with the means on board, we had the idea, whenever a ship appeared likely to pass perilously close, of shining our electric torch on the sail, thus illuminating a larger area, which must have been visible from quite a distance. I could not help feeling what a curious effect this disembodied light must cause, apparently floating between crest and trough, and wondering if we did not revive for those who saw it some legend of the sea. We must have looked like a ghost ship. On the other hand, I may be exaggerating and it may well be that we were not noticed at all.

Finally, my watch ended and Jack took over. I slept like an innocent until he woke me up on the morning of May 26. At first I could not imagine where I was. It was a feeling I had not had since my childhood, the complete bewilderment of waking up in some strange hotel room. It was a feeling I was not to have again for many months, until the morning after my arrival in the West Indies.

As we expected, the wind had veered and was edging us toward the coast. For the first time we let down our leeboards in an attempt to hold our course with the wind on the beam. This was the most the dinghy could manage, as it was incapable of sailing into the wind. The leeboards proved very effective, and although they reduced our speed to about one knot, we managed to keep a safe distance from the coast on a parallel course.

We started to feel very hungry. Until then the sensation had been no worse than that of waiting for an overdue meal, but now it became strong, accompanied by a cramp in the stomach, "a sensation of striction and torsion," as the medical books put it. Otherwise I felt perfectly well. Jack was rather more affected. He submitted passively to my proposal to make a first medical examination. His tongue was dry and coated, and there was a small rash on the back of his hands. His pulse was slow, but still strong, and there were no signs of any serious dehydration. He was thirsty but in spite of my advice made no attempt to drink anything. He should have been reassured by my example, as I took my regular ration of sea water in accordance with the figures for safe absorption I had worked out. We were both constipated, defying the gloomy prophesies of those who insisted we should include a chamber pot in our equipment. Perhaps I should explain this. The day we left a so-called specialist in the matter of lifesaving at sea had told my wife: "You will never see your husband again." When she asked why, he replied: "Insufficient preparation. They are going to be six weeks at sea and do not even have a chamber pot with them." If anyone casts doubts on this astonishing conversation, I can produce witnesses.

Thirst did not present a problem for me. It was a bearable one for my companion, but for both of us the pains of hunger became worse and worse. Each of us spoke with longing of the ham roll we had refused just before we left. The thought of it seemed much more tangible and tempting than the most elaborate imaginary dinner. This uneaten sandwich became the main reason for our hunger, and it gave me a new insight into human desires and regrets.

During the afternoon, when it was my turn to rest, I thought of all the delicious snacks we had eaten at the medical schools in Boulogne and Amiens, and every now and again the insidious thought entered my head: "Why on earth did you leave that comfortable little life and what on earth ever induced you to get into this scrape?"

Several porpoises were gamboling around us, only a score or so yards away. They seemed quite resigned to our presence and we found their company comforting. What is more, if they could catch fish, there was nothing to prevent us from so doing. It was a clear, calm day and I took a shot of them with my movie camera. Unfortunately, all we had to eat was another spoonful of plankton. We could have caught more, but the net acted as a drag, and since we were still near the coast, we did not want to spoil any favorable chances.

During the afternoon Jack surrendered to my insistence and drank a few mouthfuls of sea water. I had just explained that unless he made up his mind to do so, his system would become so dehydrated that drinking it would then be useless and even dangerous. To my great relief, he finally accepted my reasoning and took a drink. The next morning all the incipient signs of dehydration had disappeared. Even his thirst had gone. We laughed a good deal about his conversion to heresy and our spirits rose.

The nights that followed brought us a pleasant surprise. Since the atmosphere was very humid, we found that very nearly a pint of fresh water had condensed on the bottom of the boat. The dinghy had yet to ship a drop of sea water, so we managed to collect our windfall with a sponge. It was not enough for our total needs but it was a great help. Above all, it was fresh water and tasted like nectar. Toward evening the wind became exasperating. During the day it had been completely unpredictable, both as to force and direction; flat calm would be succeeded by a stiff breeze coming from all points of the compass, and the sea became quite rough. Nevertheless, the dinghy behaved very well in spite of the Mediterranean's varying moods. I was rapidly becoming confirmed in my conviction that the dinghy was the ideal form of lifeboat.

We had not seen the coast all day. We knew it was not far away, but it was hidden in a thick heat haze. Jack had been unable to take our position with the sextant, and we were not sure where we were. About six o'clock in the evening the coast reappeared, but we could not make out whether we were off Estérel or Saint-

Raphaël, or still near Cape d'Antibes. Before we could make up
our mind, the sun set for the second time in the voyage and the
lighthouses started to send out their reassuring messages. We
were between Saint-Raphaël and Cape Camarat, still fairly well
out to sea, but not yet quite safe. We were really very hungry and
faced the night with somewhat subdued optimism. For some reason or another there seemed to be a light breeze off the sea. Was
our expedition going to end by being driven ashore on Cape
Camarat as the "specialists" had predicted? There seemed little
we could do about it, so I went to sleep.

When Jack woke me up at one in the morning to commence my
watch I saw that we had already passed Cape Camarat to starboard. At least we were not going to end up there, and if we
could get past the island of Levant, the worst part of the French
coast would be behind us. It is not so easy to become a castaway.

I shall not soon forget May 27. The sun rose on a splendid day,
and during the course of it our chief anxiety was dispelled. In the
middle of the afternoon, I was dozing away with the fishing line
tied round my ankle. I soon learned that this was a stupid trick,
because if a sufficiently large fish had taken the bait, it might have
severed my foot. Suddenly there was a violent jerk on the line. We
had caught a splendid sea perch, or grouper, and we pulled it
in with feverish haste, rather, I imagine, as one draws the first
bucket of water in an oasis after crossing the desert. What a piece
of luck! The creature was carefully gutted and cut into neat slices.
We had not forgotten our civilized manners. The head half was
kept for the next day, and we shared the tail half. The sight of the
pink flesh almost made me vomit, and Jack obviously felt the
same, despite the fact that I had already tried eating raw fish in
the laboratory. It was up to me to show an example. Of course it
is delicious, I said to myself, and swallowed the first mouthful.
It really wasn't so bad. The taboo was broken. Forgetting our
careful upbringing, we tore at the flesh with our teeth, each
mouthful seeming more appetizing. After extracting the juice

with my fruit press, the rest of the fish was placed on top of the tent to dry in the sun. At the next meal it almost tasted cooked.

Each civilization has placed a taboo on certain forms of food. Would you eat locusts or white grubs? No. But a Moslem cannot eat pork. Once, in Britain, I even ate whale. Unfortunately, I knew it was whale and so thought very little of it. Plenty of people will eat horse or cat, if they are told it is beef or rabbit. It is all a question of habit. I am sure our grandmothers would never have eaten with relish a steak tartare.

The wind continued warm but feeble. However, our full stomachs had raised our spirits again. When a naval patrol boat hove in sight, presumably out of Toulon, we awaited its arrival with calm and assurance. But we knew something of the trials of Tantalus when the captain grinned and offered us a few bottles of fresh beer. We declined stoically. I do not know that this has been reported anywhere, but there would certainly have been a storm of comment if we had accepted it. The incident with the *Sidi Ferruch*, the ship we met ten days later, was sufficient proof.

After this luxurious, but largely immobile, day, a favorable wind blew up just as the sun was setting, and the lights of the land gradually disappeared in the night. Soon the French coast was out of sight. Contrary to all predictions, we had not been thrown up on it.

CHAPTER 5

On the High Seas

INCURABLE LANDLUBBERS though we were, I hadn't realized the sensation of physical pleasure which the continued sight of the land had given us. We saw it slowly disappear on the morning of the twenty-seventh with distinct qualms. Our compass course was 210°, that is to say, 30° west of south, although with a magnetic variation (or declination) of about 10° west; our true course was nearer south-southwest. This meant that we were keeping an equal distance from Corsica and Sardinia to the east and the Balearic Islands to the west. Before leaving, I had made a study of the prevailing currents and I was expecting one of them, not very well defined, the Balearic Current, to carry us in a westerly direction.

By now we had eaten the last piece of sea perch and we were going to have to fast again, although after having caught one there seemed absolutely no reason why we should not catch more. For the time being it was back to plankton and sea water, to which Jack was now perfectly resigned, so drink presented no problem.

On the twenty-ninth two cargo boats, one Greek and the other British (the *Dego*), passed quite close and greeted us. This was quite unusual, as both previously and from then on most of the ships we met ignored us completely. Whether this was deliberate or because they did not see us, I cannot say, but I became increasingly convinced that it is up to the castaway to look for help rather than rely on automatic assistance. In our case the lack of recognition was even more baffling, as ships had been advised of our expedition. I can only assume that our low position in the water made us almost impossible to see. Shipwrecked survivors must suffer from the same handicap. It is up to them to draw attention to themselves.

The wind freshened and veered during the evening and was heading us straight for the Balearic Islands. We were getting terribly hungry again. We had finished off the sea perch the night before and we had not caught another thing. It seemed as if there were no fish out to sea. We began to think of it as a watery desert. As night fell I took the first watch. At first everything seemed normal, but with my senses sharpened by hunger I started hearing strange noises at about eleven o'clock. Was I the victim of some hallucination? I was a little frightened but tried to reason things out. It was certainly no noise made by man, from whom we were now cut off except for the thoughts of our friends. The noises came from the sea around us, but it was pitch dark and impossible to see anything. I pictured dolphins and porpoises dancing a sort of saraband, doubtless in honor of our frail craft as it pursued its course. The volume of sound was so loud, so compelling, and lasted so long that astonishment and curiosity kept me awake until dawn, when it became possible to discern huge gray phantoms with a metallic iridescence all around *L'Hérétique*.

"Whales!" I cried out, jerking Jack's sleeve violently. We counted at least ten performing a stately and peaceable minuet around the boat. They must have been between sixty and a hundred feet long. Sometimes one of them swimming toward the boat would dive a few yards away. We could see his tail on one side when his head was well clear on the other. These huge beasts seemed quiet, docile, and full of good intentions as far as we were concerned. Jack was more perturbed by their presence than I was and was afraid that some brusque movement on their part might upset the dinghy. He recalled the adventure of the brothers Smith, both asleep in their yacht with the tiller lashed, who had roused a whale to fury by colliding with it and been capsized by the terrible blows of its tail. The whales made off as day broke, but Jack promised that in future he would stand watch with me if necessary, as he did not share my confidence in the good will of our nocturnal visitors. I was delighted and did not hesitate to avail myself of his offer whenever the long hours became too depressing.

Nothing of consequence happened on the thirtieth, nor did we add anything to the larder. We were slowly getting used to our abnormal existence. The chief question remaining was how the dinghy would behave in a storm. Would it ride it out successfully, as its young brother had between Boulogne and Folkestone? I believed it would, but Jack was not so sure, although he was prepared to accept the risk. In any case, it would be better to make the experiment in a stretch of sea as busy as the Mediterranean rather than fifteen hundred miles from the nearest coast.

Toward evening we saw, to our joy, the outline of Mount Toro, the highest peak in Minorca, outlined against the setting sun. It was seventy-two hours since we had left the French coast. Jack had predicted our landfall at midday, when in spite of great difficulties he had succeeded in determining our position by taking a sight of the sun at noon. This was an operation incomprehensible to me even under normal conditions, and in those in which we found ourselves it seemed more like a magician's trick. Jack had to coincide in his sextant the lower rim of the sun with the line of the horizon, not always easy to do from the bridge of a ship. Seated on an inflatable pontoon, bouncing over the waves, it was truly a miraculous performance.

"Land! Minorca!" we shouted. We knew for the first time the almost painful joy of the castaway when he catches his first sight of the land toward which he is steering. Even for us it was high time, as we were wracked by hunger. All we had had to eat for two days were a few spoonfuls of plankton. However, our troubles were by no means at an end. The coast we had sighted, seemingly within our grasp, was to take another twelve days to reach, or twice as long as the period we had already spent at sea. If we had known this, I think we would have succumbed to despair. As it was, we were already making lighthearted plans for our return to life on shore; we had worked out the wording of the telegrams we were going to send and licked our lips at the thought of our first meal in some little country inn. Then, all of a sudden, the wind dropped and the sail started to shiver. We scanned the sky, which was slowly casting over with clouds from the southeast, where a storm was clearly brewing. We quickly put out the sea anchor, as we were not yet experienced enough to leave such precautions until the last moment. Hauling down the sail, we covered in the dinghy completely and settled down to wait for the storm to pass. It is worth mentioning, in passing, that its very existence was afterward denied by the meteorological service at Monaco. Their reasoning was quite simple: their weather charts gave no indication of a storm, therefore there cannot have been one. But the Air Atlas pilots, whose route took them through it, told me that they had thought of us during this period of bad weather.

The squall soon arrived. We were cramped into a narrow space, knees bent, thoroughly uncomfortable, but at least safe. We could feel the waves breaking against the bow of L'Hérétique and the water running over our heads across the tent. It was rather like being in a giant Ferris wheel, making great swooping movements while remaining on a horizontal plane. L'Hérétique stuck to the water like a limpet, and I felt quite certain that nothing would ever affect its basic stability. It was even possible to write up the logbook. All our equipment remained firmly in place while outside the waves redoubled their fury.

We exchanged very few words to break the suspense, aside from occasional exclamations. Crouched under the tent in the space reserved for one of us to sleep, we looked at each other fatalistically. Everything was diffused with the yellow light that came through the canvas. Jack looked yellow, I looked yellow, even the air itself acquired a daffodil tinge, as we sat quite helpless amidst nature's turbulence. During this passive and exasperating interlude, we tried to guess where we were being driven by the storm. Jack covered sheets of paper with calculations of our possible drift and finally decided that we were being thrown back into the Gulf of Valencia. Picking up the *Pilot Book*, I learned that this was a dangerous area, with frequent storms, usually blowing in the direction of the Gulf of Lions to the north. It was a stretch of sea we had tried to avoid at all costs, but our intentions were not binding on the unmanageable cockleshell to which we had trusted ourselves. We committed our fate to Providence and tried to profit from the period of inaction to recuperate our strength.

In the semidarkness of the tent, our heated imaginations were prey to all sorts of fears. What would become of us in this fierce battle between the sea and the sky in which we were tossed to and fro like a sheaf of straw? We counted the hours in the hope that daylight would enable us to feel like human beings again instead of inanimate objects at the mercy of the elements.

The last day of May brought little relief, but no further danger, although we were gradually being carried away from our destination. The first of June rose on a rough, confused sea and a fog so thick you could have cut it with a knife. It was impossible to see the bow of the boat. The fog lifted slightly as the day wore on, sufficient to see a large passenger liner pass about a hundred

yards away, bound for Barcelona. The wind had settled in the
east-northeast, and we were still in danger of being driven onto
the Spanish coast. We were so weak by now that we had to take
turns about three times to pull into the dinghy the twenty-five
yards of fishing line dangling uselessly in the water. At noon
Jack tried to take our position, although the pale sun was barely
discernible through the low fog bank. This proved impossible,
and instead he tried to calculate our drift. By his reckoning we
had been carried into the Gulf of Valencia and must be somewhere in the neighborhood of a little group of islands called the
Columbretes, a few miles off the port itself. The day was going
to seem even longer and more depressing because of our en-
forced inactivity.

Suddenly a strange distant noise made us aware that something peculiar was going on. We slid out of our shelter, ready
for any eventuality, only to become transfixed with astonishment. About a hundred yards from *L'Hérétique,* to port, a strange
white mass, intangible yet vast, appeared out of the sea like some
prehistoric monster. The apparition slowly came nearer while I
feverishly loaded my underwater harpoon gun as a last desperate defense measure. Stupefied, I recognized that the beast,
some eighty or a hundred feet long, was an extremely rare albino
whale, of a type practically unknown in the Mediterranean.

Not only did we need to prove to ourselves that we had not
become lightheaded, but we would require some evidence if
people were to believe our description. Throwing down my to-
tally inadequate weapon, I seized the movie camera and recorded
the monster's menacing approach. We held our breath, expecting anything to happen. I was fascinated by the beast's red eyes,
but Jack watched with increasing terror each flick of its enormous tail, which could easily have shattered the dinghy at a
single blow. I tried to calm our fears by recalling the peaceable
troupe of whales we had recently seen, but this failed to dispel
the menace implicit in the slow approach of this solitary and un-

expected creature. It dived underneath the dinghy and then swam round us as if to show off its astonishing snow-white skin. Then it slowly turned away and disappeared into the mist.

Hardly recovered from the shock and still discussing this extraordinary apparition, we cocked our ears to a new danger. It was almost as if the whale had been the precursor of a series of trials designed to break our spirit. Barely an hour after the monster had disappeared, we heard the ululation of a siren. We both sat bolt upright. In fact, I had heard a faint sound of the sort several times already, but so indistinctly that I had thought my hearing was probably playing me tricks and had made no mention of it. It had occurred to me for a moment that perhaps we were not so far from land, but I saw no point in awaking vain hopes in my companion. Now there was no further doubt. The noise, which almost drowned the sound of our voices, could only come from some man-made device, and the effort to determine its direction made us slightly hysterical.

Tracing the source of a sound is terribly difficult in a fog. I was convinced that it came from the southwest and Jack was equally sure that it came from the northwest. Completely blind as to our true position, we unfolded the chart of the Mediterranean and, forcing ourselves to be calm, tried to determine which stretch of land we might be near. Our fingers met on the same spot: the Columbretes group of islets, about ten miles south of the position Jack had estimated.

Before we could gather our wits we were assailed by the threat of imminent disaster: the sudden throb of an engine drowned out the noise of the siren, and we took every shadow in the mist for a vessel about to run us down. It seemed that nothing could prevent catastrophe. We both clutched at something with which to signal our presence; I picked up a mess tin and hammered on it with the handle of my fish press, while Jack beat another pan with its lid. We worked ourselves up into a frenzy amidst the violent cacophony of engine and siren surrounding us. Then they suddenly cut off, to be followed by an almost palpable silence. We sat for a moment or two petrified and then redoubled the noise of our own makeshift fog signals. As if in answer, both engine and siren thundered out again. I felt I would go mad if this went on much longer. Trying to keep a clear head, I made an effort to determine the direction from which this all-enveloping volume of sound was coming. I counted the minutes: ten whole minutes which seemed the longest of our lives. Then the uproar ceased as suddenly as it had begun, suspending at the same time our own frenzied efforts.

Then, as if a magic wand had been waved, a sudden breeze dissipated the mist, leaving the horizon clear in every direction. There was nothing, absolutely nothing, to be seen. We sat in mute stupefaction. We had not been victims of an hallucination, of that we were sure, but in our somewhat weakened condition it was quite impossible to find any logical explanation for what we have since called the Mystery of Columbretes. For the time being we decided to try and forget this extraordinary occurrence in case it should give us nightmares; our most immediate need was to recoup our strength. When we returned to the matter again, each of us tried to put forward some reasonable hypothesis. The most likely seemed that we had heard a submarine surfacing to recharge its batteries, but submarines do not carry a siren. We have never solved the mystery, and it will have to remain one of the inexplicable occurrences which castaways of all time may have to endure.

Another ordeal, purely personal but no less unpleasant, awaited me. During the wild night from the first to the second of June, I had started to feel sharp, stabbing pains in my jaw, typical of a growing abscess. It soon came to a head, due doubtless to the infection of some small cut. A diet of raw fish had probably retarded its healing, as we had noticed that the slightest scratch took days to close up, with a distinct tendency to go septic. If it had happened to Jack, I would not have hesitated to use penicillin, but as I had cast myself in the role of guinea pig, I felt that this would be too easy a cure and one unlikely to be at the disposal of a real castaway. The pain soon became so unbearable that, after sterilizing my pocketknife in the flame of the oil lamp, I lanced the swelling, disinfecting the incision with one of the sulfa powders. The agony nearly sent me off my head for a moment, and Jack became seriously perturbed, but lasting relief soon came; the treatment had not been so bad after all.

We still seemed to provide an attraction for whales, which added their own noises to another disturbed night. The wind continued to blow in strong gusts, and the waves crashed over the dinghy's bow with unabated vigor, but through this endless volume of sound it was possible to hear the snortings and blowings of our giant companions. Emboldened by the night and our apparent harmlessness, they came uncomfortably close and I began to lose confidence in their benevolent intentions. I was afraid they might underestimate their own length as they dived under the boat and would surface too soon, smashing the dinghy and probably putting an end to the pair of us.

Our riding light attracted all manner of sea life; porpoises and various species of fish jostled in its rays. Then two little green lights rose behind us out of the depths. They looked like the eyes of a cat lit up by the headlights of a car. It was a small ray, which I tried to harpoon without success. It was probably just as well as the flesh is almost as salty as the sea itself and might have damaged our kidneys. What was more unfortunate, in moving about the boat I knocked one of the oars into the sea. This was serious as we only had two and we were now unable to row the dinghy. We flashed our torch over the sea, but it had disappeared. We now had to rely entirely on the wind to beach the boat.

The next day, June 2, the sky had cleared, but the wind, although it had veered to the southwest, was still very strong. We were being forced inexorably into the much-feared Gulf of Lions, and Jack estimated our drift at about fifty miles a day. We had eaten nothing for five days, and our hunger had become almost insupportable even though its symptoms had changed. We no longer suffered from stomach cramps, but from increasing lassitude, an overwhelming desire to do nothing whatsoever. Photographs we took at the time show us both sunken-cheeked and tired out, with bags under the eyes. My face was swollen out of shape. All we both wanted to do was sleep. I was dozing about nine o'clock in the morning when Jack, who was at the tiller, cried out:

"Alain, Alain, a fish."

I jumped up and saw another sea perch idling in our backwash between the points of the floats. He was a big fellow, weighing at least ten pounds, swimming with his snout almost on the steering oar, under which he ducked from time to time to scratch his back like a pig against its pen. Whatever happened, we had to catch him. My harpoon gun was loaded and ready, and in a flash I had it aimed over the stern. The instant it touched the water, the fish, in a moment of fatal curiosity, moved in to see what this new object was. I pressed the trigger and the arrow buried itself five inches in his head, killing him instantly and tinging the sea with blood. Hoisting our prize on board, we sat there blankly for quite a while, devouring it first with our eyes. This was probably a good thing, for it enabled our stomachs to adjust themselves again to the idea of food.

Something to drink was our first requirement. As this was a good-sized fish, I decided to test the method of dorsal incisions, rather like cutting the bark of a rubber or pine tree. The fresh liquid gave us an almost voluptuous pleasure, but the flesh did not prove too easy to digest. After all, most stomachs would rebel at a diet of raw fish followed by a fast and then raw fish again. But our morale recovered at a bound. We now had food for two days. The storm was still tossing us about, but the weather was getting warmer and the outlook distinctly more favorable.

As it happened, the next three days showed little improvement. The wind continued to blow from the wrong direction and we ran out of food again. We had not advanced a single yard toward our destination and on the morning of the fourth day we were faced by the prospect of another period of fasting. This was almost more than we could bear and it did not seem likely that we would be able to carry on very much longer. The Mediterranean just did not seem to provide the means for survival. Several ships passed with a rumbling of engines, but none of them appeared to see us, or, if they did, made no attempt to alter course. We did not hail them, and for all we knew it would have had no effect. However the time was rapidly approaching when we would have to try.

On the morning of June 5, the eleventh day of the voyage, the weather calmed down, leaving us exhausted, starving, but still confident and determined to go on in spite of it all. The first problem was to find out where we were. At noon Jack was able to fix our position for the first time in six days. We were one hundred and fifty miles north-northeast of Minorca. The storm had driven us in a great arc. We were going to have to cross the very course we had held a few days earlier, but with typical Mediterranean moodiness the wind had suddenly died away. There was not a breath of air.

The sea had become completely calm, a mirror broken from time to time by leaping black objects which left concentric ripples. We were surrounded by tunny fish and porpoises, jumping in every direction. The whole sea was a veritable larder and somehow or other we had to get our hands on the food there. When I think of my efforts that morning, I have to smile. I had made up my mind that I would try and harpoon a tunny fish. Only a starving man would try anything so bizarre. Hitting one did not present much difficulty, but my fellow underwater fishermen will appreciate only too well the problem involved in bringing in the catch. I put on my goggles, adjusted the respirator, and lowered myself into the water with Jack handing me the gun. I did not have to swim far to reach the shoal of tunny fish. "Brrrm!" The harpoon quivered in one of the fish, but it was much more as if he had caught me, as he set off dragging me behind him. Fortunately, even a nylon line has a breaking point and it soon snapped. Empty-handed, I swam back to the dinghy and with Jack's help managed with difficulty to climb on board again, having lost only my illusions and a harpoon. It cost a considerable effort to hoist myself over the float and I thanked God for my companion, as I would never have been able to make it alone.

Our fast continued, June 4, June 5, June 6. . . . The days grew longer, more monotonous, and even more exhausting. A small ration of sea water was our only drink and the plankton our only food, although we ate a little more each day. Every movement became a painful and superhuman effort. Hunger had become starvation and our acute condition became chronic. We were starting to use up our own store of proteins, feeding on our last physical reserves. We did not think about it much, as we were dozing or sleeping three-quarters of the time.

The wind was fickle, but we were making some headway in the right direction. On Friday evening, June 6, we made up our minds to try out our signaling apparatus. If we succeeded in stopping a boat, it would prove that we could attract its attention in case of distress. We would also be able to send news to our families. We knew they must be worried to death and we were afraid they might ask for an official search to be made for us, which would have meant the end of the experiment. The Mediterranean was proving a good trial run, as we had hoped, but the question of mere survival was not paramount. In fact, this cannot be said to be a problem in the Mediterranean, where survivors must very quickly be rescued by one of the countless ships which use it. On the other hand, in a great, lonely ocean like the Atlantic it would become the dominating factor. Now that both crew and equipment had undergone their first test, we were in a hurry to get to

Tangier or Gibraltar and start the most important part of the voyage. Jack did not want to delay this until September as he was convinced that the hurricane season then commenced in the West Indies. As a matter of fact, it ends in September. Hurricanes are unknown between November and March. How he came to make this mistake I have no idea.

With all this in mind, we decided that we would stop the first ship and, if necessary, ask for a few rations. It had never occurred to us to broach our own stock of condensed foods, as these were very difficult to come by and would have to be reserved for a real emergency in the Atlantic. There would have been no point in using them for day-to-day needs and they were only there in case we could simply hold out no longer. Since our general health was still quite good, we had not even discussed the idea of using them, as the experiment would thereby have lost all point. About six o'clock a vessel hove in sight on the starboard bow. We had already planned how we would try to attract its attention. First of all, Jack set off two explosive rockets. The ship gave no sign of having seen them. I then took the heliograph, a device which works on a mirror principle, sending a beam of light into the eye of the observer, and tapped out S O S in Morse. Still the ship held on its course. It seemed absolutely impossible that we should not have been sighted, but that is the only explanation, although it is almost beyond belief that someone, even one of the passengers, should not have noticed us. It held firmly on its course and disappeared over the horizon, leaving silence once again to descend on the calm sea. However, if humankind was indifferent to our fate, the creatures of the sea did not abandon us.

The evening closed on a strange and unforgettable sight. Just as the sun was setting it was reflected in a thousand dancing pin points on the sea. As I looked at this sparkling mirror I realized with astonishment that it was made up of hundreds and hundreds of turtles, their shells, seemingly cemented one to the other, forming a solid crust on the waves. Every now and again a head would appear out of this mass, darting wicked little gargoyle's eyes at us. One brusque movement on my part as I tried to harpoon one of them and the whole mass disappeared as one, like a sheet of metal oscillating into the depths. Then night, indifferent to calm and storm alike, fell and enveloped us.

Saturday, June 7. Day broke in torrid heat. Only the barometer, falling steadily, caused a pessimistic note. Jack was still asleep. I woke him in a low voice: "Jack, there is a boat about two miles away." He grabbed his rockets and fired them off, one, two, three. In spite of the explosions and the shower of sparks which lit up the dawn, the ship held on its course. It was too early for me to use the heliograph. What were we to do? Was this ship going to get away too? Does a castaway have to give up all hope of being seen? As a last resort we had a smoke bomb, visible by day, which enveloped us in an orange cloud as soon as we threw it into the sea. We waited, each second seeming like an hour, but as the smoke cleared we saw that the heavy bulk of the ship had turned in our direction. To our surprise, the liner, called the *Sidi Ferruch,* made no attempt to slow down.

Once within hailing distance, the captain shouted from the bridge: "Is there something you want?" rather as if we had stopped him to say, "No, thank you very much." "Please report our position and let us have a few emergency rations," we replied. The liner then stopped her engines and circled away to stop about five hundred yards off.

In spite of my exhaustion I had to use the rudder oar as a scull. We reached the side of the ship and exchanged mild conversation with the passengers and the first officer, who passed us down some food and water. Then the captain appeared. "Come on, come on, we have no time for experiments," he shouted. A perfect gentleman, in other words. Jack frowned but said nothing. He had not had a smoke for five days and was hoping at least to be offered a cigarette, but he was not going to ask for one. The first officer speeded things up, but no attempt was made to invite us on board. Then off went the *Sidi Ferruch* with her amiable captain.

We did not know how dearly we were to pay for this meeting or how we were to be reproached for accepting this pitiful little stock of rations. Everyone chose to forget that we had spent ten days out of fourteen without food or fresh water and that on the other four we had only had raw sea perch and fish juice. The mere fact that we had accepted this minimum assistance branded us as impostors, although our experiences had not differed so greatly from the survivors of *La Méduse*. We had held out for a whole fortnight. In spite of their wine and water, most of the survivors of *La Méduse* were dead when they were picked up on the twelfth day.

CHAPTER 6

Capsize

THE *Sidi Ferruch* STEAMED rapidly away. I hope, my dear captain, that you will never have to make any "experiments" yourself. Little did we realize what a cargo of mocking laughter, calumny, and even insult you carried off with you to rebound on our unlucky heads during the coming months.

Jack gave vent to his fury at the French captain's lack of courtesy and I could only second his remarks. However, there were compensations: our friends and families would be reassured; we had resisted the temptation to transfer on board; we knew again the exquisite pleasure of drinking fresh water; and had a high time exploring the sack of provisions. It contained sea biscuit, four tins of bully beef and one of condensed milk.

The barometer had not lied. In spite of the brilliant sun, the wind had freshened again, but this time from the right direction —it was driving us south-southwest, straight for Minorca. At midday on Sunday, June 8, the summit of Mount Toro appeared again on the horizon, much more clearly defined than eight days earlier. Were we going to be able to land this time?

The Balearic Archipelago consists of six islands, of which

the three largest are Majorca, Minorca, and Ibiza. Minorca is the most easterly of them. Its capital is Mahon, on the southern part of its east coast, famous for a battle fought there by the Duc de Richelieu and also for the delicacy we call mayonnaise, originally mahonnaise. We could choose between Mahon and the little port of Ciudadela on the west coast. It is quite impossible to effect a landing on the north coast, which is composed entirely of steep cliffs, scene of many shipwrecks, the best known being perhaps that of the *Général Chanzy* in 1910. We therefore had to clear it one way or the other.

We steered first for the northeastern point of the island, hoping to make Mahon during the night, but the wind played us false and we drifted farther to the west, finding ourselves not more than a few cable lengths off the north coast by morning. Heaven knows there was little enough sign of the flower-bedecked inlets conjured up by the name Balearics. The coastal resorts are all at the southern end. For three interminable days we drifted past the cliffs without any hope of landing. We were extremely close and I had the movie camera working overtime. If the wind blew us offshore again, we would at least be able to prove we had been there.

During the course of Monday we drifted slowly toward the northwestern point of the island. We were so close that I could see a rabbit run across one of the stretches of green. Hunger was no longer a problem. I was out fishing underwater every day, bringing in a rich harvest. During our passage along the coast and during the whole of our stay, I spent an hour with the harpoon gun every day, never bringing back less than fifteen pounds of fish.

We were now in a hurry to make harbor. The Mediterranean voyage seemed to have no great point any more, and we wanted to be shipped as soon as possible to Málaga or Tangier or somewhere close to the Strait of Gibraltar. We would then be in a position to start our crossing of the Atlantic.

Tuesday the tenth, found us at sunset a few score yards off the northwestern point. The gentle breeze which had brought us thus far suddenly died down just as we were rounding Cape Minorca. There was not a single bay or inlet in which we could anchor, and, to make things worse, the land wind started to carry us out to sea again. It looked as if Minorca were going to disappear below the horizon. Were we really going to start the vicious circle of the Gulf of Valencia again? We tried to stop our drift with the sea anchor, but the current carried us to the north as well, and on the morning of Wednesday, June 11, the eighteenth day of the voyage, we woke up to see with despair that we were fifteen miles off the coast on which we so longed to land.

Then our spirits rose again. A little sea breeze carried us in once more toward Cape Minorca. Once we had rounded it we knew that Ciudadela was only about a mile to the south. About ten o'clock, to cheer us up still further, we saw about a dozen fishing smacks coming up the coast and then dispersing in all directions. None of them seemed to notice us, but one of them went to lift its lobster pots to our northeast. It could not fail to meet us on the way back and we intended to ask for a tow into the harbor. In the meantime we had not been sighted and we had to concentrate on rounding the cape. Just as we thought we had made it the wind abandoned us again. Were we going to go through the whole weary round again? Fortunately not. Just off the coast a fishing boat came up to us, passed us a tow and in less than ten minutes, as if in a dream, we made our entry into the little port, which in a matter of minutes was to adopt and seduce us. The attractions were to prove dangerous for my companion, who, although a model of courage, endurance, and even temperament at sea, was unable to resist the temptations on shore.

Our arrival soon attracted most of the population. Waiting for us also on the mole was an elderly Spanish officer with an extremely intelligent face. As soon as we clambered ashore he came up to me, supported as I was on my shaky legs by some friendly spectators, and said:

"Are you French?"

"Yes."

"Where are you from?"

"From France."

"With that?" he asked, looking at *L'Hérétique*.

"Yes."

"Out of which port?"

"Monte Carlo."

"Sir, do you expect me to believe that . . ."

I gave him a newspaper cutting with an account of our intended departure.

Then, looking at our little flag, this splendid old officer took a step back, saluted, and said:

"Eh bien, Messieurs, vive la France!"

Deeply touched, I asked him to note that the seals on our emergency food stocks were unbroken.

What a contrast with the preceding forty-eight hours! Our first task was to send off telegrams to our families. Then we drank a huge glass of iced beer, which tasted like the nectar of the Gods, served in a little café whose proprietress took a maternal interest in us during the whole of our stay.

It felt like being transported to fairyland. Our first guides became our firm friends and showed us all the treasures and charms of their little town. Guillermo is one I still think of, who took us into homes with wonderful souvenirs of Moorish, French, British, and Spanish conquerors, with magnificent Queen Anne furniture, Spanish coats of arms, and superb Flemish manuscripts. On the first day he said to me: "This house is yours," a phrase which in a man of his race means what it says. Then there was Augustin, who introduced me to some typical Minorcan dishes, particularly *Sobrasada* (a highly spiced sausage cooked with plenty of peppers), which is still such a delicious memory; and Fernando and Garcia, who showed me little inlets where sea perch, mullet, and bass restored confidence to a fisherman too long unsuccessful.

Even my love for music was catered to. Guillermo took me on the following Sunday to meet a Minorcan composer, who had staying with him the superb Majorcan pianist Mas Porcel, a pupil of Alfred Cortot, who filled my head again with the wonders of Bach, de Falla, Schumann, and Debussy. Never has it been so difficult for me to leave any place.

However, the next day, assisted by our fishermen friends and encouraged by *Adyudante Militar de Marina* Manuel Despujol, the officer who had received us so charmingly on our arrival, we left this enchanting little port amidst the applause of its inhabitants. A sardine boat towed us about five miles out to sea in the direction of Alcudia.

The operation was now becoming familiar. After about half an hour the tow was dropped and we were alone again. This time we did not have far to go: our next destination was Majorca, about forty miles away. With luck we should be there in the early hours of the next morning. The chief problem was to avoid being carried to the north, no easy matter as our leeboards, having been indifferently mounted and used with insufficient care, were of little use now that the wind was blowing from the southeast. Nevertheless, everything went well and on the morning of Tuesday, the seventeenth, we found ourselves right on course. We passed several sardine boats, which greeted us in a friendly fashion. We had accustomed ourselves very quickly to life on board *L'Hérétique* in spite of our spell on land. We had taken some food with us, as there seemed no point in adhering to our spartan regime during such a short passage and we wanted to keep the emergency stocks intact for the Atlantic. About six o'clock, Minorca disappeared below the horizon to the east and the majestic peaks of Majorca stood out against the setting sun. Everything was going splendidly, and we soon picked up the lights of Alcudia at a distance of about five miles.

Jack, who was at the tiller, broke the silence. In his usual calm fashion he said: "Alain, we are drifting to the north, and quickly at that. The wind has veered due south. I don't like it at all, these north and south winds cause bad storms in the straits here. However, we'll try and make it."

The rocky escarpments of Majorca slid away from us. Was it back to the Gulf of Valencia again? There was only one solution, the sea anchor. What an infuriating sea, we thought. Would we never get out of it and into a region of regular winds? I swore that I would never sail the Mediterranean again without an auxiliary motor. We were faced by another night of inactivity, with no idea of what the morrow might bring. We were getting heartily sick of the Mediterranean. We were both up at the crack of dawn on the eighteenth, looking round apprehensively to find out where we were. The wind had dropped, but we saw, with despair, that we were about in the same position as we had been on Tuesday, the tenth, at the same time, perhaps a little farther out: twenty miles to the northeast of the northwestern point of . . . Minorca. Rounding the cape, crossing the straits, we had to go through the whole thing again.

To crown our misfortunes, the wind sprang up from the north and rapidly freshened to gale force. In the open sea, out of reach of the coasts, we would have had nothing to worry about, but with rocks and cliffs in the offing it was extremely dangerous. There was only one thing to do: make for Ciudadela again and wait for the weather to calm down. There was no time to waste, for the wind had become very strong, but in about four hours we were close to land again. But the sea was very rough and it was clearly impossible to round the fatal cape. As we were turning east to look for some sort of shelter, we met a fishing boat which passed us a tow. Conditions were by no means good; with each wave the tow slackened and then tightened again with a violent tug.

It was not so bad heading into the waves, but Jack did not hide his disquiet. "Sometime we have to turn beam on to round the point," he said. He spoke not a moment too soon. The tow tightened just as we were on the crest of a wave, which then broke on us. In a flash *L'Hérétique* had turned turtle and we were in the water. I was swimming strongly when I heard Jack shout: "The rope, Alain, the rope!" I looked around for a length of line to throw him, although in some surprise, for he was a good swimmer. Then he explained: "There is a rope around my legs. I can't swim." Fortunately the fishing boat had come around and took us aboard. While I was still half in the water I shouted: "Jack, we are going on, aren't we?" And he replied, with true British calm: "But, of course." What a splendid fellow he was. At sea there was no one to beat him. It was a pity that now and again we had to go ashore.

L'Hérétique looked like a tortoise turned over on its back. Every now and then various objects floated out of the tent. Braving the danger, which increased every minute, of being blown onto the coast, the Spanish fishermen circled around the "wreck." Every time something floated to the surface I dived in to rescue as much as possible. First of all came the sail, then the watertight bags (heaven be praised, the exposed films were saved), then came more reels of film, the rudder oars, the sleeping bags. . . . Gone for good were the camera and movie camera, the radio set, the compass, and the binoculars. The mast was broken and the tent torn. We entered Ciudadela with *L'Hérétique* in tow and our own tails between our legs.

What had happened? We had been towed too fast in a position neither our sail nor sea anchor permitted us to take up. The combination of wind, direction of tow, and a maliciously breaking wave had been sufficient to capsize the dinghy. We had learned one lesson for all time: never to drift even with a favorable wind without streaming the sea anchor and taking the waves on the bow. Our lives were saved, the boat was intact, and our will to go on unaffected, that was the chief thing.

CHAPTER 7

Tangier Interlude

As SOON AS we had disembarked I sent off a telegram asking for replacements of the essential equipment we had lost. The reply was soon received: "Jean Ferré on way to Palma." This meant that Jean was probably already there and we could relax for a day or two to await his arrival. On Thursday morning I set off early for a long day's submarine fishing.

I was swimming around with Fernando, the local champion at this sport, when a small boy arrived with a message that two Frenchmen, with news of my wife, had arrived and were asking for me: "That must be Jean. He has made good time," I thought. Mounting a borrowed bicycle, I pedaled for three miles under the torrid sun, only to find when I got to the port that they were two strangers who had got hold of Jack's logbook and were copying it out in the most impudent fashion. They turned out to be reporters. I made an effort to be polite to them and tried to give them a full account of our experiences. They already knew most of the details as they had questioned the harbor master and read through the logbook. They interrogated me the whole morning and then followed me to the house of friends who had invited

Jack and myself to lunch, where they took photographs of us without so much as a by-your-leave. I learned that they did not even know Ginette's address, let alone have news of her, but they seemed in no way abashed and finally took off for Palma, leaving us all flabbergasted. We decided there and then that we would never put ourselves out again for the press.

On Friday morning the same thing happened. Two more Frenchmen arrived and demanded to see us. We went into hiding, only to be discovered an hour later by Jean Ferré and Sanchez, the French Consul at Mahon, both breathless, sweating, furious, and convinced that we must have a touch of sunstroke.

The news they brought was bad. The expedition's backer declined to help us any further. What had caused this sudden decision? Those newspapers which had never taken us seriously had announced after our meeting with the *Sidi Ferruch* that the Bombard expedition had failed. We had to get to the bottom of it. . . . Leaving Jack in Minorca, I decided to return to Paris via Majorca. There I received every help from M. de Fréminville, the French Consul, and left on Monday, June 23. It was a hair-raising journey. Picking up a car in Valencia at eight o'clock in the morning, by twelve-thirty I was in Madrid; by seven in the evening at San Sebastian; and at six o'clock the next morning in Poitiers. Something of a record in itself.

In Paris the battle started. All I wanted was enough new equipment to make us ready for sea again, but no one took us seriously any more. The air was thick with rumors of other expeditions. Someone was going to try and paddle from San Sebastian to Dublin in a canoe; another enthusiast had thought up the idea of pedaling across the Channel in a water scooter. Jack and I were lumped together in the same category. Everyone just laughed at us, and the people who had built the dinghy, even though they had not completely lost confidence, hesitated to assist us further. Our backer, subdued by "specialists" who contended that they had been right all the time, refused to put up another penny, under the pretext of not wishing to be an accessory to my "suicide." I could not make him realize that all he was doing was to diminish our margin of security, as we intended to go on in any case. What had gone wrong? Why was everyone trying to stop the expedition?

It was no easy thing to track down. However, it was clear that a certain number of people had expected us to be driven in a matter of days onto the Italian coast. Now that there was a reasonable possibility of our success they were getting worried. For my part, I was not out to prove the efficacy of certain lifesaving equipment, but most particularly to show that however slim it was, the castaway had a chance of saving his skin. Certain third parties started to interest themselves in the affair, but I could only guess at their influence until our arrival in Tangier, when it became fully apparent. The whole expedition was in danger, although after long-drawn-out discussions I did manage to get a few spares. I left for Palma de Majorca again, exhausted and demoralized, on Sunday, June 29. Jack was to load *L'Hérétique* on board the ship *Ciudadela* and join me there, and we would then start off again in an attempt to get as near as possible to the Strait of Gibraltar. If we were held up for any reason, we would, if necessary, take ship as far as Tangier. Once there, people could think what they liked, but it would be difficult to stop our embarking on our Atlantic adventure. My chief fear was that means would be found to have my sailing license canceled. That really would mean the end of the expedition. It was not that people might say: "He has not been able to carry out his experiment," but: "There must be something wrong with his theories or he would have been able to prove them by now." I really think it was fear of this second argument which gave me the strength to carry on.

Our spares arrived by plane: a mast, two leeboards, a compass, and a few handbooks. What trouble they caused us with the Customs! Without the help of M. de Fréminville I think we would still be arguing. Finally they were brought along to the yacht club, which generously offered us hospitality, and by the next Sunday morning all was ready. Jack had decided to leave late at night in order to take advantage of the land wind to carry us out into the bay. For once we had made up our minds to leave the harbor under our own power. Our departure was much more informal than the first from Monaco. Jack and I were at the oars. A small launch from the club kept us company for a little way. A breeze sprang up from the east. It was good-by to Majorca. We were on our way again, bound for Africa or the Spanish coast, depending on the wind.

This lap was a pleasure cruise. On the Monday morning, not far off the island, I caught some big mullet. The food supply was assured. It was a magnificent day, the wind was driving us along in splendid fashion, and Jack had high hopes of making Alicante, on the southeastern coast of Spain, whence we intended to hug the coast as far as Málaga. But whatever happened we had decided that if the wind should drop, we would take advantage of the first opportunity to ship *L'Hérétique* and ourselves to Tangier. The sooner we passed the Columns of Hercules and reached the Atlantic the better. The Mediterranean was beginning to give us claustrophobia and we needed the broad ocean to insure the success of the expedition.

The weather was getting distinctly hot. I swam every day, but Jack preferred to remain in the boat. During the evening Majorca slowly disappeared from sight and we set course to pass as far as possible to the south of Ibiza. On Tuesday morning we could see its coast on the starboard bow. The wind continued favorable and underwater fishing provided us with a positive feast of fish, while schools of porpoises paid us frequent visits. About four o'clock we realized with some anxiety that we were making very little headway in spite of the favorable wind. A contrary current was holding us back.

If the wind had turned foul, we would have been thrown back

to Majorca. We decided to make for land and beach *L'Hérétique* at the first convenient place. We got out the oars again, but it was hard work and we were not offshore until nearly nightfall. The sea was pitted with rocks and reefs, but with the last gleams of daylight we found an enchanting little bay of crystal-clear water and pulled *L'Hérétique* ashore. We were about fifteen miles from the capital of the island, but it was a warm, starlit night and we looked forward with pleasure to sleeping on land. We had now given up all idea of beating farther around the Mediterranean and had made up our minds to take the first available ship.

A charming farmer invited us to drink some wine with him. It was acid and proved a powerful purgative, but he was unique. He was completely ignorant of what was going on in the world and had never even heard of Truman, Stalin, and Eisenhower. We could hardly believe that such a thoroughly self-sufficient person still existed in the world. Stretched out on our couch of pine needles under the stars, it seemed as if we were on another planet.

The next morning Jack asked me to catch some more fish. I dived in and was back almost immediately with a handsome bass. We spent the whole of Thursday and Friday in idyllic inactivity, surrounded by high red cliffs and exploring a sea bed as multicolored as a coral atoll, scintillating with the reflection of hundreds of fish catching the sun's rays. It came almost as a disappointment on the Saturday when, at six o'clock in the morning, the wind sprang up from a direction which should take us to the port of Ibiza. As we rowed out it seemed almost a sacrilege to break the mirrorlike surface of the lovely little bay, to leave such a haven of peace for the fury of the open sea. Once out of its shelter we had to pull on the oars a good bit harder, for the wind had died down again. By midday it had veered in the wrong direction and we had to seek shelter again in the little bay of Es Cana, near an islet called Tagomango.

We were developing quite a taste for these unscheduled calls, and with his usual insouciance Jack was starting to ask why we ever needed to put to sea again. On the evening of July 12 we were accosted by two civil guards, one of whom caressed his rifle and said:

"You are forbidden to land except at a port. You must put to sea again immediately."

"That's impossible, the wind is wrong," I replied.

"That's not our business," he said, red with anger.

"Very well, gentlemen, come out with us, you will see."

That struck home, and these two examples of the typical police mentality found nothing more to say. After consultation with their headquarters, they gave us permission to wait for a favorable wind.

The next morning I was looking for our lunch when my submarine horizon was transformed by the sight of a magnificent pair of legs. They belonged to Manuela, the eldest of three Chilean sisters. The swim ended by our becoming five and lunching off a huge watermelon. Manuela had brought with her a copy of Mallarmé, which I leafed through.* These lines caught my eye:

> . . . *Je partirai! Steamer balançant ta mâture,*
> *Lève l'ancre pour une exotique nature!*
> *Un ennui, désolé par les cruels espoirs,*
> *Croit encore à l'adieu suprême des mouchoirs!*
> *Et peut-être les mâts, invitant les orages.*
> *Sont-ils de ceux qu'un vent penche sur les naufrages*
> *Perdus, sans mâts, sans mâts, ni fertiles îlots . . .*
> *Mais, ô mon coeur, entends le chant des matelots.*

> . . . I will start! Steamer balancing your masts,
> Heave anchor to reach a nature exotic!
> Ennui, devastated by my cruel hopes,
> Still believes in the handkerchief's final adieu!

* Lines from "Sea Breeze," included in *Mallarmé: Poems.* Copyright 1951 by New Directions.

And perhaps the masts, inviting tempests,
Are of those which a wind bends over shipwrecks
Lost, without masts without masts or fertile isle . . .
But oh my heart listen to the sailors' song!

The weather was changing again and the tops of the trees were leaning toward the west. The wind had returned, so we left and the same day entered the harbor of Ibiza, where the yacht club received us with characteristic Spanish hospitality. On Friday we embarked on the *Ciudad de Ibiza,* which took us as far as Alicante, and from there we just managed to pay our fares as deck passengers, without food, on the *Monte Biscargui* to Ceuta. Regarded at first with some suspicion, we were marvelously treated by the crew. The passengers promised to take me to a concert if ever I should pass through Bilbao. The first engineer showed us around all the ports of call and we made great friends with the radio operator, who nevertheless confided to us in his cups one day that he considered us *un poco locos* (a little crazy). The captain offered me a replacement for my tattered shirt and the radio operator gave Jack a pair of shoes. One of the stewards saw that we did not go hungry.

Now that our Mediterranean voyage was nearly over, what conclusions could be drawn from the first part of our experiment?

First of all, the problem of drink. For four days in my case and three in that of Jack's we drank sea water, from May 25 to 28. During this period our urine was perfectly normal and we had no sensation of thirst, but it is essential not to wait for dehydration before drinking sea water. We always found that a good remedy for any feeling of thirst, especially when our faces were in the sun, was to cover them with a towel or piece of cloth soaked in sea water. Two days on sea perch provided us with food and drink, but care had to be taken not to compensate too quickly for our fast. Six more days of sea water followed, bringing us to the safety limit, and then two more days of fish without any internal complications. In other words, out of fourteen days we drank fish juice for four and sea water for ten. By interrupting the consumption of sea water we were able to double what I considered the safety limit.

Secondly, food. The symptoms of hunger were cramplike pains extending to the shoulders during the first and part of the second day. On the third day these pains ceased and were followed by somnolence and a permanent sensation of fatigue. To reduce the need for food it is essential to induce an effect of physical hibernation by leading a vegetative existence. Our blood pressure hardly varied, but in this respect I do not think the experiment lasted long enough for concrete results. There was considerable danger of ophthalmia and conjunctivitis due to the reflection of the sun on the sea.

I noticed none of the effects normally associated with the consumption of sea water and neither my companion nor I experienced vomiting or diarrhea. On the contrary, we were subject to persistent constipation, without pain, and coating of the tongue or mucous membranes or bad breath, which lasted twelve days. However, we both suffered continuously from wind. We had no fainting spells (lipothymy), and although our skins were dry from the third day onward, there was no sign of petechia (red patches on the skin). No edema of the ankles, although for two days my face swelled up, as is evident in the film I took. Cuts were slow to heal and had a distinct tendency to turn septic.

On the fifth day I developed an abscess of the first lower molar on the right side, which came normally to a head, although it left a hardening and generalized pain. There was slight drying of the mucous membranes, especially the lips, but only at the start.

I do not propose to enter here into further details, but I would like to say a few words about my equipment and my companion. The dinghy did all that I expected of it; in spite of heavy seas it proved completely seaworthy at all times. Only two items needed strengthening: the mast and the mountings for the lee-boards.

Jack was the perfect crew. In sailing from Monaco to the Spanish coast he was responsible for a feat which many people, with knowledge of the sea, considered impossible. Most of them expected us to turn up in Corsica or Sicily. As a companion, he was active, brave, and unselfish. He always chose the uncomfortable jobs and places for himself and was always ready to cope with emergencies. He never complained and never seemed more pessimistic than the situation appeared to warrant. He proved that it was possible to determine a position from a completely rudimentary craft, never lost confidence and was the ideal companion for such an adventure. Jack Palmer would have remained with me and even been the driving force if only I had foreseen that too long an interval on land would lead to his discouragement and final abandonment. He brought me as far as Tangier, the steppingstone for my great Atlantic adventure. Without him I would never have got there.

Ceuta at last! It was a public holiday. No one was at work and the captain refused to go on and drop us in the bay of Tangier, declining to listen to our arguments. In the end the radio operator intervened on our behalf and the captain agreed to take us on to Tangier providing we obtained triple authorization from the police, customs, and port authorities. It was ten-thirty in the morning and the ship was due to leave at three o'clock in the afternoon. As we went ashore we heard the captain guffawing: "Well, they'll never get them. Three passes from three different offices on a holiday! They won't be bothering me again!"

By twelve-thirty we had got them all. The Spanish authorities carried out all the formalities in response to our oral requests, and the harbor master had an order for us to be dropped off at Tangier entered in the log of the *Monte Biscargui*. In fact, we did not leave until nine o'clock, but about half an hour later, with

L'Hérétique already inflated on deck, we were hoisted over the side by a crane. The captain had considerable doubts as to our fate, telling us that he would have thought twice about launching one of the ship's boats, as there was a high wind such as always churns up the water of the straits into choppy waves and flying spume. The *Monte Biscargui* gave us a last salute on her siren and we were left in the dark to make for the lights of the international city. There I was to find many true and generous friends, but also redoubtable enemies who were to separate me from my companion.

We arrived in Tangier at midnight and found our way through the murk to the yacht club. At long last our Mediterranean journey was over. Tangier is a large and handsome town where national prejudices have long since lost all significance. When I called at the French Consulate the next morning to pick up my mail, M. Bergère, the Vice-Consul, helped me to get a plane ticket to Paris, payable on arrival, and then M. Mougenot advanced me the money to pay for it. The people at the consulate were also good enough to lend me sufficient money to buy a decent suit of clothes and check into a hotel. On Monday, July 28, I left for Paris, but as far as Jack was concerned it was a fatal error on my part, as the delay was to lead to a severing of our association. If we were to make the Atlantic crossing, it had become essential to replace *L'Hérétique*. There was no point in embarking on such an expedition without having everything possible in our favor. Not only had our inflatable dinghy carried us more than a thousand miles in the Mediterranean, but it had been in service for three years previous to that. I knew our patron had ordered a duplicate, and I was determined to have the use of it.

I got to Paris the same day, only to find the atmosphere even more frigid than during my previous visit. No one was prepared to put up another penny. In a long session with our sponsor I gave him an account of our initial findings and enumerated all the reasons why it was essential to continue. At the end of our interview he opened his arms to me and said: "Whether you go on without me or not, I will help you all I can."

He gave orders that the new boat was to be delivered to me. The expedition was to continue after all. We agreed to dine together, but in the meantime something else went wrong. He had changed his mind again, although I was never able to discover why, and now refused to let me have the boat. Moreover, he did everything in his power to dissuade us from going on. As a concession I managed to get him to agree to accompany me back to Tangier, where I was sure Jack would be able to convince him.

Before we left we had several conversations with experts and engineers, whose interest in our preliminary results ought to have been sufficient persuasion in itself. But as far as I could make out he was much more interested in discovering whether it would be possible for castaways to use a patent vaporizer or a battery-driven distilling apparatus. There was even a motor worked by a piece of cord which ran around the boat. And all I wanted to do was to prove that it was possible to live at sea without food or patent appliances of any sort. We had seemed to share the same objective at first, but now our intentions had clearly become quite different. In the end, I got the new dinghy direct from the manufacturers myself and flew back to Tangier with it. Our patron was with me and on our arrival we had a long conversation with Jack. The pair of us had to listen to a long disquisition based on the official theory that an inflatable dinghy would never hold together longer than ten days at sea. We were the wrong people to tell that to, and Jack became very angry. This seemed to prove the turning point, and I thought our patron had come around again. He suggested buying us a radio receiver so that we would always know the exact time at which to take our position.

"They are pretty expensive," I told him.

"How much?"

"Here in Tangier, about fifty or sixty pounds."

"And in France?"

"About twice as much."

"I'll buy you one."

We went to the dealer, our patron paid the bill and had it made out to Doctor Bombard, Museum of Oceanography, Monaco. The next day he left . . . taking the radio with him.

PART THREE

ATLANTIC

CHAPTER 8

Lone Voyager

It was at this point that I began to notice a change in Jack. Little by little his enthusiasm was ebbing. I learned some time later that he had told one of our friends: "If Alain keeps us here much longer, I shall never be able to leave. . . ."

In the meantime, offers of help continued to arrive: M. Clemens made us a present of fishing tackle, the Swimming Club received us in princely fashion, Mougenot contacted one of General Leclerc's old radio operators, named Le Guen, to get us a wireless set, M. Tarpin, a stationer, gave us a pair of binoculars, and M. Bergère helped us out in a number of ways.

In spite of all this active assistance, the wait became interminable. Jack always found a new reason for putting off our departure, either the wind, the tide, or the weather. He was the navigator and I had to conform. But one day a taxi driver told me what everyone in Tangier seemed to know, apart from myself. Jack had made up his mind to prevent me from continuing and was convinced that I would never attempt it alone. Terribly disheartened for a moment, I was on the point of giving up. But then I thought what people would say: "You see, there is nothing in it, the whole theory is nonsense." I knew it was sound and to prove it I meant to go on.

Brought to the point, Jack finally agreed, but without any enthusiasm. First of all, he suggested that we should stay in the Mediterranean, but I insisted on our original plan. The American Naval Attaché, with whom we discussed the matter, waved a handful of pilot charts and pronounced firmly that we would never get as far as Casablanca, much less the Canaries. These pilot charts are specially edited by the British and American navies and brought up to date every two or three years. They give full information about the prevailing winds and currents, although outside certain clearly defined areas the information is subject to local fluctuations. I insisted that what we were trying to do was feasible. I had studied the ocean currents for a whole year in the Museum of Oceanography. It was not too late in the year and I was convinced that over the next month we stood the best chance of success.

After objecting again to the state of the tide, the winds, and the lack of charts, Jack agreed, with some bad grace, to make a start on Monday, August 11. Knowing that he was by no means convinced, I started to worry myself; all he had to do was to alter course while I was asleep and I would wake up again in the Mediterranean. If we were going to have to spend our time watching each other we might just as well give up the idea of setting off. However, the wind had become favorable and was likely to hold for about three days. Here was an admirable opportunity to pass the Strait of Gibraltar and defeat the current which flows constantly into the Mediterranean. We were towed out by a Spanish ship, but imagine my anxiety when, instead of making for the west and the Atlantic, Jack gave orders to set course for Cape Malabata. This was off to the east, toward the Mediterranean, but he told me we needed to seek shelter until the wind had died down a little.

The sea was certainly quite rough, but if we did not take advantage of the favorable wind, we would never be able to pass the narrows. Somehow the straits had become a symbol. I knew we had to force this passage, to leave the Mediterranean behind and venture out into the limitless ocean. The Atlantic had swallowed up the whole continent from which it took its name, and we were going to brave it in a tiny dinghy. Here indeed was a challenge.

The Spanish ship carried us steadily eastward, and we finally stopped off a little beach, almost underneath a house belonging to a friend named Count Ferreto Ferreti. We spent the whole of Tuesday in idleness. On Wednesday morning, the wind was still in our favor, but Jack set off for Tangier about nine o'clock to make a few last-minute purchases, with the intention of returning as soon as possible. It was the last day of favorable wind we could expect, and it meant leaving by six o'clock in the evening at the latest. When the time came there was still no sign of Jack. I was all strung up, feeling that if I hesitated all was lost.

I scribbled a note for Jack: "I am taking the responsibility of leaving alone. Success can come only if we believe in it implicitly. If I fail, then it will be the fault of a nonspecialist. Au revoir, old friend. Alain." This I gave to a Customs officer named Jean Stodel, and then, with his help, put out to sea, borne along by a combination of anger, ambition, and confidence.

My first task was to pass the straits and gain as much sea room as possible in order to pick up the Canaries Current. Because of my inexperience, I was afraid of hitting the coastal rocks and so tried to keep as far out to sea as possible. In fact, this hazard worried me much more than the specter of loneliness. I had to win this first round. Passing from the Mediterranean to the Atlantic is no simple matter. It's like leaving one world for another. A difference of a few miles involves entering another dimension and another age. Even the terms of reference change. Time must be counted in weeks instead of days, and distances in hundreds of miles instead of miles. Moreover, to effect the passage in a craft like mine meant undergoing an almost impossible ordeal, like some story from the *Arabian Nights.* Anyone who has seen a river burst its banks or the sea pour through broken dikes, with the great flood of water uprooting everything in its path, will have an idea of the strength of the powerful current against which I had to fight. The great salmon of northern waters have, to help them in their struggle against waters of this force, the superhuman, tireless strength which comes of their love and mating instinct. To help me through the straits I had my love of adventure, my burning desire to reach the open sea, and the challenge of the ocean, which thrust itself at me as if to deny me any possibility of success. Happily, I had another ally to help me fight this barrier: the east wind, blowing only for predictable periods. Wind against current, that was the contest in which I had to become the master. That first night I did not dare take a wink of sleep. The slightest inattention on my part would have found me driven back into the Mediterranean. The wind blew strong the whole night as I skimmed over the surface of the current. There was certainly no lack of light, with all the ships crisscrossing around me. I gradually lost sight of Cape Spartel. When I glimpsed it again through the morning mist to the southeast, it seemed that I was well past it.

During the morning while the wind appeared to have blown itself out, the current seemed to redouble its efforts. I tried to get across it. I made distance to the south all right, but the land seemed to be sliding away to my right. I was absolutely exhausted, but I knew I had to complete the passage or give up altogether. I was convinced there must be some way of breaking through. Cape Spartel loomed larger and larger, but when I glanced at the compass I saw to my horror that the point of the cape was to the southwest. It was no good. I was right back in the straits. The Gibraltar Current, full of miniature whirlpools, was buffeting my little craft. In my despair, I remembered from canoe trips I had taken as a child that it is always easier to make headway against a current nearer the shore. The mass of Cape Spartel grew larger and larger. Then I caught my breath. It seemed as if a large white villa directly on my beam was falling slightly behind. After a few agonizing minutes, hope became certainty. I was slowly creeping past the cape, and, amidst the splendor of the setting sun, on that memorable Thursday, I entered the promised ocean. A small countercurrent, an offshoot of the great hostile flood in the center of the straits, had come to my rescue and carried me to the rendezvous with my great adventure.

SPARTEL BANK

Thursday 14th: 10 am

CURRENT

WIND

Wednesday 13th: 8 am

CAPE SPARTEL

Friday 15th: 10 am

CAPE MALABATA

TANGIER

Now that I was beyond all doubt in the Atlantic, the first attack of loneliness replaced the hours of tension. I recognized the feeling as an old enemy. It does not come in a sudden attack, but I was to know its insidious creeping effect during the long Atlantic days. While I was still near the coast, I knew I could hold it at bay. Its full effect would only come when I was on the high seas. In any case, I had many immediate matters to attend to, more than sufficient to take my mind off the obsession with loneliness which in due course was to become the only problem and the only companion on board.

The first thing I had to decide was where I was going. Should it be Casablanca or the Canaries? On the face of it, the best alternative was Casablanca, but I had to take into account the reactions my solitary departure might have caused. There might well be people who considered me a dangerous lunatic whose boat and equipment should be confiscated in his own interests at the first landfall. It occurred to me that I might be well advised to touch nowhere, but then I dismissed the thought. My wife and friends would be in a ferment of worry, knowing that I was alone. Then I realized that a much more dubious thought had entered my mind: after all, if they do stop me it won't be my fault. It even gave me a certain feeling of relief. I did not let the idea develop, but I recognized that my subconscious fears were at work.

For the immediate future, I had to avoid being blown ashore on the nearest coast, the eventuality which most of the "experts" would be expecting now that I was alone. With a wind from the north-northeast, I was able to set a course roughly west-southwest. If I could hold it, I would be able to follow the chord of the coastal arc between Tangier and Casablanca.

The next thing to master was the art of navigation. I understood the use of the compass and the sail. I had with me a Cras ruler with which to determine my course. After a few tentative experiments, I found I could make it work. The principle was simple enough. All that was necessary was to place its point on the next meridian (or parallel) to the south, and then read the resultant figure, which gave the theoretic course. Then it was a question of adding the declination according to a table, which gave the true course.

I spent the whole day of Friday, the fifteenth, familiarizing myself with the use of this instrument. I saw very few ships. Fortunately, the fishing lines with which M. Clemens had supplied me were proving extremely efficient. The catch consisted

chiefly of ray's bream (the *Brama raii*). At least I had plenty
to eat and drink. I thought of Jack and what a shame it was he
was no longer with me. He had become discouraged at the very
moment when the expedition had acquired interest and purpose.
Now I was a real castaway. I began to keep a daily record of my
blood pressure and pulse.

The following day, Saturday, the sixteenth, a ship altered course
to hail me. It was a big trawler out of Algeciras, and the crew was
duly astonished at the quantity of fish I had been able to catch.
This had provided me with some distraction from my struggle
with the wind, which was proving exasperating: it sprang up
regularly about midday from the right direction and died down
with equal regularity about eight o'clock in the evening. In the
meantime, I started to work at the sextant. There seemed no great
trick in measuring the height of the sun at midday: all I had to do
was to adjust the instrument until the lower edge of the sun co-
incided with the horizon in the eyepiece. The scale then gave
the angle between the sun, the observer, and the horizon, but
that was only the beginning. From this reading I somehow had to
calculate my latitude.

With a little experience, I soon learned how to do this with
the help of the navigation tables I had with me. I did not need
to know the exact time. All that was necessary was to read off
the angle when the sun had reached the summit of its trajectory.
At least it was enough for the time being, as I was sailing more
or less straight down the same meridian of longitude (Tangier
lies roughly 8° 15′ West, and Casablanca 9° 50′ West, a difference of just over a degree of longitude, which I could afford to
ignore), and I was therefore able to disregard this factor.

Every day I checked the readings the sextant had given me by
comparing them with points on the coast I could identify on my
chart. This enabled me to confirm my calculations, or rather, as
far as the first few days were concerned, to invalidate them. At
midday, by rare good fortune, the sea was usually perfectly calm,
and the line of the horizon showed clear and steady.

During Saturday I saw several aircraft on the regular Casablanca run and they helped to reassure me that I was on course. Even so, I felt terribly alone. I began to debate in all seriousness whether I ought to continue or give up when I got to Casablanca. To be quite honest, fear, or at least a rising state of anxiety, began to get the better of me. As long as I was within easy reach of the coast, nothing much could happen, but after that? Every time I looked toward the broad Atlantic I was appalled by its immensity. Its expanse simply bore no relation to the sea I had just left.

But by Sunday, the seventeenth of August, I was another man. It was still barely light when I woke up, and then, like a flash of lightning far off in the sky, I thought I saw a flying saucer flash across my field of vision. I grabbed my camera to film it, only to realize my mistake. It was the planet Jupiter, which a roll of the boat had suddenly endowed with movement. I found the whole episode terribly funny, and confidence returned with my good humor. How little is needed to change one's mood. Over the course of the months to come my morale came to depend more and more on the quick caprice of minor pleasures and disappointments.

The day soon settled down to its usual monotony; a few ships passed and every now and then a plane. I caught no sight of the coast, but at least I knew it was there, and this certainty buoyed up my confidence. During the evening, three lighthouses sent their friendly personal message of identification. I took two of them to be Medehia and Port Lyautey. I crept into my sleeping bag in an optimistic frame of mind.

I slept like a log every night, with my rudder and sail lashed in position. Even so I woke up fairly regularly, twice or three times a night, just long enough to glance at the compass and sail, see if there were any lights on the coast, assure myself that all was well, and then sink back to sleep amidst a calm there was not enough breeze to disturb. It was as if the wind hesitated to interrupt my slumbers. But the morning of Monday, the eighteenth, brought a disagreeable surprise when I found myself enveloped in a thick sea mist. At least it taught me the value of the compass.

With nothing else to do, I tried to learn something about astro-navigation, in order to be able to determine my position without depending exclusively on the midday sun. Unfortunately, my handbook was in English, and its authors seemed intent on explaining why certain things should be done instead of describing how to do them. I got thoroughly confused, but not unduly depressed. Nevertheless, the sound of foghorns echoing through the mist started to get on my nerves. It was no longer just one, as in the incident at Columbretes, but an incessant chain of noise and echo. They sounded for all the world like some weird race of animals talking to each other, and they brought home to me, perhaps for the first time, how completely alone I was. I began to think back on the physical presence, the point of reference, the sort of ever-present life belt which my companion had represented. If only he would agree to team up with me again at Casablanca or in the Canaries. Amidst the loneliness everything seemed unreal and mocking. I wanted terribly to have someone there who would confirm my impressions or, better still, argue about them. There in the fog I began to feel that a mirage would appear substantial and that I would be incapable of discerning between the false and the true. I began to think of only one thing: stopping at Casablanca and not moving another yard. I felt a terrible need for human company. Although the mist was lifting I could catch no sign of land and could distinguish no lights. I was absolutely alone, the land was hidden and the lights seemed to be out. I was on the verge of complete discouragement when a tanker emerged from the mist and passed quite close:

"Casablanca?" I hailed.

"Keep on the same course. Bon voyage," they called back.

I spent most of Tuesday in a rage, which served to keep up my spirits. The days were still made up of eight hours of wind and sixteen of calm. It seemed as if I would never pick up the trade winds. The number of aircraft appeared to increase, still confirming my course. I was getting near, of that there was no doubt. If only the wind would hold, I should make Casablanca that evening or the next morning. I worked out a whole series of calculations in an attempt to decide how long I was going to need to get from the Canaries to the West Indies. As far as I could make out, it was going to take fifty or sixty days. My morale started to rise. I was still catching any amount of fish, and one big ray's bream fell right on top of me. In order to get out of my wake it had jumped, the wrong way, to its misfortune. I began to think how splendid it would taste fried.

At two-thirty in the afternoon I caught the reflection of the sun from the Fedala reservoirs and made a note in my log: "Fresh water this evening or tomorrow."

At eight-thirty I was a hundred yards from the Casablanca mole. I had missed the entrance to the harbor, and the swell prevented me from seeing the navigation buoys. I decided to spend the night outside. The sound of waves breaking on the mole was not exactly reassuring, but I had quite a good night's sleep in spite of this. However, it is much easier to sleep on the high seas than near the coast. For those who sail the oceans, the land is much more dangerous than the sea.

Wednesday, the twentieth, brought a flat calm, so when I woke up I got out the oars and rowed vigorously to the yacht club basin. My arrival created a sensation. I was shown the morning paper, which carried a banner headline: *"L'Hérétique* lost in the Gulf of Cádiz." Perhaps I had been luckier than I thought. M. Auradoux, the special commissioner, arranged everything with the police and Customs. (No easy matter for someone returned from the grave.) Dr. Furnestin, head of the Moroccan Fishery Board, presented me with a net for catching plankton. But I shall have more to say later about the wonderful reception I received in Casablanca. I had made up my mind, whatever the circumstances, to leave the following Sunday, the twenty-fourth, at ten o'clock in the morning.

CHAPTER 9

Casablanca—Las Palmas

THE WHOLE PURPOSE of the expedition came under discussion again. Two men in particular, who had gone into every aspect of the project and interrogated me on every point, ended up by saying, "Go ahead, all is well." They were Dr. Furnestin and a mining engineer, Pierre Elissague. We were surrounded by new friends, all listening, uneasy and anxious, but expressing no opinion. They made no attempt to influence my decision. But three men were against the whole thing and tried to discourage me by pontificating about the dangers ahead: the club president, the lifeboat coxswain, and the owner of the launch which was supposed to tow me out to sea again.

I was alone in the lounge of the club, when I heard two journalists talking.

"We might as well leave. He is not going to start," said one of them.

"What do you mean?" I interrupted. "I am only waiting for this fog to disperse to start my tow."

"You are not going to get a tow," they replied.

The president had posted a notice that the owner of any launch which towed me out would have to surrender his club burgee, a penalty which was equivalent to expulsion.

I went along to see the president and told him: "I do not want to cause trouble, but I am going to find a tow. If I drown, you will be able to say that you opposed my departure."

Putting down the charts and instruments I was carrying, I stamped off in a rage to find someone who would take me out to sea. Jean-Michel Crolbois, owner of one of the two yachts in the basin, agreed to do it.

"Would someone go and get my charts?" I asked, turning to the crowd of journalists and others who surrounded me.

The charts were brought back by Gisèle Vallerey, the swimming champion. The newspapers embroidered this incident by commenting: "You can see the fellow is a mountebank; he even forgets his charts."

We hauled out slowly from the port with an escort of launches. I waved to my friends, and we slowly lost sight of each other in the mist. I find these entries in the detailed log I started to keep of my lonely voyage:

"*Sunday, 24.* Cast off tow, off El Hank, flat calm. Mist. Cramp in the stomach, but not hungry in spite of all the tunny fish frolicking around me. Mist thickens and wind drops as night falls, illuminated by precise and impassive winking of El Hank lighthouse.

"*Monday, 25, morning.* Same place, wind freshens from right direction, NNE, but what a mist. Impossible to tell distance from coast.

"*1400 hours.* Coast in sight due south. What can it be?

"*1800 hours.* Think it must be Azimur. Almost too good to be true. Fish to keep myself occupied. Should see Sidi-Bou-Afi light in fifteen miles. Ought to be to the southwest.

"*2100 hours.* There it is, right where it should be. Fair enough.

"*Tuesday, 26, morning.* Mazagan abeam. Weather very clear.

Should be able to round Cape Blanc from the north. If I don't drift, I ought to keep steady course of 240 for seven days. Provided I have the courage. Sextant becoming an old friend. Mark the chart. Ought to see Cape Cantin light this evening. That will be last view of land until Canaries.

"*Evening.* Coast seems to be moving toward me, although my course is parallel to it. As night falls, still no sign of Cape Cantin. Light has a range of thirty miles so must still be some distance away. Magnificent fishing at dusk: bonito and ray's bream.

"*0100 hours.* Cantin light to SSW. Fine!

"*Wednesday, 27.* Coast very clear. Wonderful visibility. Recognize it all from the coastal elevations in my *Pilot Book.* Cape Safi in sight. Have logged sixty miles a day, except Sunday. Any amount of splendid fish. Now starting to lose view of land. Must hold course WSW for six days. No weakening. First danger will be that pointed out by Furnestin: difficulty of passing between Cape Juby and Fuerteventura. Decide to keep as far west as possible. Coast toward Mogador still clearly discernible. Fortunately, the *Pilot Book* describes it as visible far out to sea, which is reassuring. Use of the sextant becoming more complicated; having doubts about this longitude business. Seem to be drifting to the west, but wind falls again at night. Not exactly helpful to navigation by dead reckoning."

I find it impossible to reread without a slight retrospective shiver this phrase in my log:

"*Thursday, 28.* Last brief view of Mogador, then nothing but a blur. Wind very light, seem to be drifting to the west. Full of hope.

"*3 o'clock.* Wind freshens from NNW. Must watch the drift as I do not want to get too far south. Horribly alone. Nothing in sight. Complete novice as a navigator. Do not know where I am, but only suppose I do. If I miss the Canaries, then I am in the South Atlantic, tragic route of the raft of *La Méduse.* Wonderful wind. If only it holds!

"*Friday, 29.* Wind has kept steady. Have even had to take a reef in the sail.

"*9 o'clock.* Big cargo boat passes, exactly on inverse course. Must come from the Canaries, so feel I am heading the right way. If only I did not have this problem of how to land. . . .

"*Saturday, 30.* Lord, what a night! Feel pulped and did not sleep a wink. Squall blew up about 1600 yesterday; had to put out sea anchor. It seems impossible: (1) that a vessel as frail as this can weather the battering of the sea; (2) that my heart can hold out. Morale low; really think I shall have to call it off in the Canaries. If only I can get some sleep tonight. Still nagged by this terrible fear of passing between two islands without seeing them, either to left or right.

"*Sunday, 31.* Drifted farther to the south during the night than I expected. Stopped a Portuguese boat at 1500; confirmed my position. Tried to offer me food and water. I refused; from this point of view all is well. Am catching magnificent mackerel every day and am really getting used to raw fish. Atlantic water tastes absolutely delicious compared with that of the Mediterranean. Much less salty and quenches my thirst perfectly. The question is whether things will seem as rosy if this situation lasts several weeks. Course seems good, am seventy miles NNE of Allegranza. If I can keep on the *qui vive* for thirty-six hours, I shall be in the middle of the archipelago. Provided, God help me, I don't sail straight out again. A flock of enchanting little black and white birds comes to keep me company every evening at exactly four o'clock.

"*Monday, 1.* Have passed one of the worst nights of the whole voyage since Monaco; sea appalling. But I have received due compensation. Yesterday evening, when I turned in, commending myself to the Almighty (I lash the helm and then drop off to sleep), I said to myself: 'If my navigation has been correct, I ought to see the first island tomorrow morning on my left'; and this morning when I woke I saw, twenty miles off to the south, on my left hand, the two islands with the charming names of

Allegranza and Graciosa. What a splendid omen! Now it is up to me not to make a mess of the landing. Full of confidence. I have won the first round and I shall win the second.

"*Tuesday, 2.* Appalled to see what a distance separates the islands and the terrifying void which will swallow me up if I miss the coast. It is quite impossible for me to retrace my steps, something I shall have to bear in mind. Once I have left the Canaries, or if I miss them, there will be no possibility of return. The minimum distance to cover will be 3,750 miles. Convinced I can make it, but there is still the problem of the acute anxiety I would cause my wife and friends, not to mention the triumph which would be enjoyed by those who predicted I would never reach Las Palmas. If I want to triumph, I must provide the proofs. I said I would arrive at the Grand Canary; I will land there and not drift away. It would have been a relatively simple matter to land on the first islands I sighted, but I must prove I can go where I wish. That is essential for the castaway, who, like me, must be able to reach the point he has selected.

"*Afternoon.* My inflatable dinghy, generally considered unsteerable, astonishes me more every day. Every morning about eleven o'clock, I have to deflate it slightly so that the air expanded by the sun does not burst it like a balloon. I blow it up again every evening. Ship practically no water and sleep peacefully. The first few nights were difficult. I woke up with a start every few moments with the sensation that some catastrophe was about to strike, but I have gained confidence. If it does not capsize during the day, why should it do so at night? Cannot possibly sit day and night with my hand on the tiller. Have realized that with the wind from aft, the dinghy will sail straight before it, with or without fixing the rudder, and have learned to trust in the steadiness of the wind. Can sleep perfectly soundly away from the land, but what is going to happen when I have to steer for shore? Impossible to sail into the wind; the most I can do is to keep it on the beam.

"*Wednesday, 3.* God help me, what is going on? Spent the whole night on the lookout for the Las Palmas light; must be there but cannot see a thing. What on earth am I to do? Ought I to stop and wait for the fog to lift? Or ought I to keep on to the south?

"*Noon.* The first clue: an aircraft passes to the right; it was still climbing after the take-off; the land must be there. I shall make it after all.

"*3 o'clock.* It is no good; cannot possibly make the coast. I thought the plane had taken off from the northern part of the island, and now that the coast emerges through the haze I see that I have drifted past twenty-five miles of coast and only have about six left on which to make a landing. Wind from the north; am drifting to the south with a strong current. I shall pass about three miles from land, but I can never reach it.

"*6 o'clock.* Perhaps, after all, I have a chance; a countercurrent is starting to compensate my drift. The southern point of the island, looking out on the immensity of the South Atlantic, is still to my left. Maybe . . ."

I still had some reason to hope when I wrote those words. At about 2000 hours I was not more than a hundred yards from the beach, but I was so terrified by then that I thought seriously of abandoning the boat and swimming ashore. The chief problem was not to be torn to pieces on the rocks. Some fishermen had caught sight of me, and a gathering crowd pointed out a spot where I could beach on sand between two reefs of sharp rocks. I finally made it. It was the first time that a rubber boat had proved it could be steered for nine hours in an unfavorable wind. I had been so paralyzed with fright that it was several hours before I could walk properly. But at least I had landed on the island I had named as my destination.

I had proved not only that I knew how to navigate, but that I could make very good time: I had taken exactly eleven days (from August 24 to September 3) to get from Casablanca to the

Canaries. Gerbault had taken fourteen days for the same crossing, Le Toumelin twelve, and Ann Davidson twenty-nine.

The navigational problems I had surmounted were: for the first time in my life I had steered by instruments on the high seas. However, as I had no particular confidence in my sextant readings, I had maintained a parallel set of dead-reckoning figures. I made a note each day of the number of miles I estimated I had covered in the direction indicated by the compass. That gave me a theoretical position which took no account of the possibility of drift. I then allowed myself a margin of safety, based on my probable rate of drift, taken from the force and direction of the current given in the *Pilot Book*. It was a factor which could not be ignored, even though there was no physical sign of its presence. This treacherous force, as real and as intangible as molecular motion, was gradually carrying me to the south and could have resulted in my passing between the islands and the African coast. Every day, therefore, brought me three possible positions: one I had calculated, one I had estimated, and, most pessimistic of all, the possible true position if all the unfavorable elements had played their part to the maximum. Bearing this last point in mind, I had concentrated on avoiding the Atlantic now always open before me.

"But," it may be asked, "since you had set off to cross the Atlantic, what would it have mattered if you had missed the islands and carried on with the most important part of the voyage?" A valid question, but there were three good reasons for stopping: first of all, the anxiety of friends and family, who assumed that this leg would only take less than a fortnight; secondly, the consideration of morale: if I had missed my first target, I would have taken it as a very bad omen. Finally, the thought that if there had been no news of me for a fortnight, the authorities would probably institute a search. They might or might not have found me, but if they did, it would have been the end of the experiment; if they did not, few would have believed in my good faith on arriving in the West Indies seventy or eighty days after my departure from Casablanca.

Eleven days' sailing had brought me again on terra firma. The little village of Castillo del Romeral, about ten miles south of Las Palmas, gave me a princely reception. When the dinghy was sighted, the inhabitants came flocking to the beach, convinced that I was a real castaway. I was therefore greeted on the beach by a sort of general assembly from the village and surrounding farms: simple, welcoming people, colorfully dressed, all waiting for me.

The coasts of the Grand Canary are extremely rocky, and although I had succeeded in landing on a small section where sand predominated, there were plenty of sharp outcrops menacing the inflatable dinghy. It only had to move a few feet to the left or right to be punctured. The bystanders soon solved that problem. With its little tricolor flag flying proudly, *L'Hérétique*, still fully loaded, was lifted onto the shoulders of twenty strong men and carried farther inshore. Two more of them helped me to stagger beside it. Manuel, the local "chief," came up and asked the expected question: Where had I come from? I gave him the usual answer in my best Spanish:

"*De Francia, de Niza, después Baleares, Tanger, Casablanca y once días de Casablanca aquí.*"

It was clear that he found this incomprehensible. He looked around to see if anyone else had heard my incredible statement. *Aures habent et non audiunt.* I could see that their native politeness to a guest was tinged with a certain skepticism. It took several days to convince them that what I had said was true. Manuel took me to his home, where I was immediately served with a fried egg; we were joined by the local medical attendant-cum-schoolmaster. In spite of my overwhelming fatigue and sleepiness, I had to spend the whole evening telling my story in an improvised patois of Iberized French, which my companions somehow managed to understand.

CHAPTER 10

Temptations of Terra Firma

I TRIED TO FIND out how to get to Las Palmas to cable news of my arrival and make contact with the French and Spanish authorities. My friends reassured me; a car (with the delicious nickname of "The Pirate") would be available the next day to take me to the capital. Manuel was as keen as I was for me to get in touch with the authorities. He wanted to be relieved of the responsibility of my presence, or at least regularize my position with the Customs and the police. A month or so earlier a yacht called *The Dandy*, coming from Finland via Casablanca, had been wrecked on the same part of the coast. With the innocence common to fishermen in every country, those of Castillo del Romeral had salvaged most of the jetsam and had seen nothing wrong in quietly retaining the greater part of it. Manuel himself had had some difficulties with the coast guards. He wanted no repetition of the trouble on my account.

In the meantime, I had to get a night's sleep. The question was where. In the school? There was no proper bed, so I stretched out on the table used for rolling bandages. There was not much give in it, but I have spent few better nights on a superbly upholstered innerspring mattress. The only trouble was that the earth seemed to have acquired a peculiar rocking motion, and at one moment I almost felt seasick.

The next morning, September 4, "The Pirate" was there waiting for me. Manuel protested loudly when I made an effort to pay him something. A final wave, and I was off.

The island unfolded before me in all its savage splendor. Bare and menacing pinnacles of rock dominated what I took to be old lava beds, on which were perched enchanting little villages. Young girls with fresh faces were out drawing the day's water (its supply is apparently the major problem of these Fortunate Isles). With arched backs and proud bearing, they seemed to walk without effort, carrying on their heads the most diverse variety of vessels, ranging from the classic earthenware jar to corrugated iron drums.

This part of the coastal plain is covered with banana trees, and I soon became familiar with the green shrubs, with flat leaves, condemned to a short life by their growth cycle. Each bush grows for one season and then has to make way for its successor. One slash from a billhook cuts short its ephemeral existence, leaving the shoot which has grown under its shadow to grow for another short span. There are very few trees, because of the shortage of water; but the date palms appeared particularly attractive, accustomed as I had become to my liquid dessert.

In due course a twin-towered cathedral in the distance announced the proximity of Las Palmas. I had read about it in my *Pilot Book*, which described the church, visible from the sea, in such detail, that my guides were convinced that this could not be my first sight of it.

Las Palmas itself has a magnificent port, the Puerto de la Luz, one of the great harbors of the Atlantic. I went straight to see the harbor master, brother of a well-known heart specialist. He was expecting me. Some journalist friends from *Le Petit Marocain* had flown over a few days earlier from Casablanca on the first flight of the *Armagnac*, a large cargo plane inaugurating a new service. They had looked out for me all the way over, and after seeing no sign of the raft, had made inquiries about me on arrival. So nearly everyone knew about my trip.

Before embarking on the next and major part of my journey, I asked the harbor master to check my sextant so that I might avoid any errors in calculation.

"With great pleasure," he replied.

Certain newspapers reproduced this incident thus: "He asked for some lessons in navigation. The harbor master refused, not wishing to contribute to his suicide." When this appeared in print, an engineer wrote to me offering the necessary instruction—a more practical way of preventing disaster. As I lost his letter, I was unable to thank him. If he reads these lines, I hope he will accept them as an expression of my gratitude.

While I was still with the harbor master, the French Consul came to look for me; it was the beginning of a delightful friendship. M. Farnoux was a second father to me, putting me up in the Consulate and introducing me to the charms of the island. He had not been long in Las Palmas himself, but when I went to his office for the first time, the most important businessman in the French colony on the island, M. Barchillon, came in to make my acquaintance. We became an inseparable trio. M. Barchillon constituted himself our mentor, and with his help all doors were opened to us. My circle of French friends was soon increased by the members of the yacht club. Unlike most such institutions, three-quarters of its membership consisted of real yachtsmen and only a quarter of loungers. I cannot possibly name all those who helped me, but I must mention Collachio, Caliano, and Angelito, who entertained me so charmingly and made my stay so delightful that it became almost impossible to leave.

I had decided not to return to France but to stay about a week in the Canaries for minor repairs, putting everything in perfect order there, rather than battling at home for additional equipment. The Consul approved of this decision, but my other friends, Barchillon and, above all, the senior pilot, Angelito, begged me to think things over carefully before setting off.

"I know the sea," Angelito said. "What you have already done is magnificent. You have more than proved your case, but believe me, there will be no fish to catch in the middle of the Atlantic."

Angelito meant well, but he did not realize he had raised the one objection which I could not afford to ignore. If I had stopped then, there would be more than enough people to say on my return:

"That is all very well, but off the Continental Shelf there are no fish to catch."

The second and more important part of my experiment was yet to come. I had already proved that it was possible to survive on raw fish; what I now had to demonstrate was that it was still possible to catch the fish in those parts of the ocean which orthodox minds contended were barren.

The Consul and Barchillon understood the reason for my determination and went out of their way to help me, the one in his official position, the other with his resources. I was only waiting for a telegram from Ginette saying "Au revoir." It did not arrive for a day or two, and I had time to cruise in a yacht toward Fuerteventura. Still nothing came. Finally, one morning, a telegram arrived at the Consulate: "Happy to announce birth of Nathalie. Our congratulations to *L'Hérétique*."

My new daughter must have recognized her responsibilities and made an effort to be there for the great day of departure. The temptation to return to France now became too great. I felt I could not possibly set off without seeing her. When I announced in the club my intention of paying a quick visit home, those who, out of friendship, had tried to dissuade me from continuing my trip thought that they had triumphed, Manuel, the old friend from Castillo del Romeral, made a special journey to the Consulate to ask: "Is it really true that Bombard is giving up?"

Farnoux gave him an evasive answer. At bottom, I believe they all thought: "He is perfectly sincere when he says he is going to continue, but we can be sure that his wife will now stop him from embarking on this folly."

Through the good offices of the Consul, a place was booked for me on the direct Las Palmas–Paris plane, and on September 12 I left. Passing through Casablanca, a crowd of friends was there to greet me at the airport.

There was a further surprise at Orly. Two journalists were waiting for me. Some of the newspapers were already saying that I intended to give up now that my child had been born. But nothing could shake the courage and faithful self-abnegation of my wife. She was confident, had seen me at work, knew that what I was attempting was possible, and understood my purpose: to save lives, thousands of lives. Not that she was happy to see me leave, but she saw the necessity for it and knew that I must complete my voyage to prove my case. She made no attempt to restrain me.

Then I became involved in the last act of what I have called the Comic Interlude. The day after my arrival, two gendarmes knocked on the house surgeon's door in Amiens where I was staying temporarily.

"We wish to speak to you in private," they said to me.

I remained silent.

"This is the point: there is a matter of eight thousand francs in costs to settle. You have not paid them and you will have to come with us to the clerk of the court, or go to prison."

"Prison for how long?" I asked.

"Twelve days." And they showed an order for my arrest.

I just did not have that much time to spare for prison. So I paid up the eight thousand francs, a splendid piece of financial assistance to the expedition.

Freed at last from vexations, I spent three delightful, mollifying days. However, the newspapers took up again their cry: "He will not resume his voyage," while Palmer went on record in Tangier as saying: "It would be suicidal madness to set off from the Canaries at this time of year." The expedition was surrounded by an atmosphere of skepticism. The birth of my daughter was regarded as the decisive factor. In the meantime, I pottered around, went to see a sick friend living near Poitiers, and then took the plane back to the Canaries via Casablanca. I wanted to spend a few days studying plankton in the research department of the Moroccan Fishing Board and go rather more deeply into the question of the fish I was likely to catch in the waters I was about to cross.

I had also made up my mind to get a wireless receiving set. I had given up the idea of a transmitter, even if one had been offered to me. My reasoning was: I would be completely alone on board, because there was now no question of Jack's rejoining me, and I had no intention of finding a successor. It would therefore have been extremely difficult, if not impossible, to work a generator while I was transmitting. In any case, I was incapable of repairing the smallest defect, and one missed contact would have convinced everybody that I was dead. The strain on my family would have been too great.

On the other hand, a receiver would be very useful. Longitude is determined by the difference between solar time at any given point and Greenwich Mean Time. There is a difference of four minutes for each degree of longitude, that is to say, an hour every fifteen degrees, and I could carry in my head the jingle, Longitude West, Greenwich Best, Longitude East, Greenwich Least. A radio receiver would render me less completely dependent on my chronometer. I could check it against radio time every day, but I would need a set able to stand up to the conditions. Unfortunately, funds were low.

I would have to trust to luck. Perhaps in Casablanca someone would help me out.

I had hardly anticipated the warmth of my welcome. There

were over a hundred people waiting for me at the Casablanca air-port, including an extremely attractive young lady with a bouquet of flowers in the colors of the City of Paris. There was a fine old regular naval officer, an expert in lifesaving at sea, who had taken up the cudgels in my defense when someone had said to him: "It is prayer books he needs, not navigation manuals." He told me that the newspaper *Le Petit Marocain,* indignant at my episode with the two gendarmes, had opened a subscription list to pay my fine. The first donation had come from Admiral Sol, naval Commander-in-Chief in Morocco, and the total was growing fast. At last I was going to be a man without a police record. One might call it the end of the Comic Interlude.

I was inundated with invitations, especially from the navy. My friend Pierrot lent me his apartment, the Fishery Board wel-comed me with open arms, and I started to look for a radio. I suf-fered no loss of weight during my stay. One group of friends who invited me to dinner at eleven o'clock at night were surprised at my lack of appetite. They did not realize that in order not to offend anyone I had already accepted one dinner invitation for seven o'clock, and there is a limit to one's appetite. The problem of the radio was soon solved. My friend Elisagne and his alter ego, Frayssines, offered me a superb battery set which is still in front of me as I write these lines. They had made for it a completely watertight nylon cover, which even protected the telescopic aerial. They even presented me with some small rubber articles usually used for another purpose, in which to keep dry the silica salts, which I was to use for dehumidifying its interior.

As a final honor, an invitation arrived one morning to visit Admiralty House. I was received by a small, brisk gentleman, dressed in tropical whites, who, with all outward friendliness, sub-jected me to a searching interrogation. He questioned me about my aims, my means, set me navigational posers, in other words, extracted every ounce of information. I can only record now, Admiral, what pleasure you gave me that day. I had been waiting for a long time for someone in authority really to seek the truth of what I was driving at. At the end of this friendly but searching session, the Admiral said to me: "We understand what you are after and we are going to help you."

Admiral, it was thanks largely to you that I had the feeling every time I met a foreign ship, Spanish, British, or Dutch, that I was a unit of the French navy.

The Admiral gave me his own marked Atlantic navigation manual and was the only professional sailor to write to me before I left: "You will succeed." *Scripta manent*, Admiral, as you knew when you did me the honor of writing a dedication on my chart.

There were, in fact, two other friends who sent me encouraging farewell letters, Jean Merrien, author of *Navigateurs solitaires*, and Jean Laurent, director of the Laboratory of Hydraulics, who wrote: "When you have succeeded, which you will . . ."

But the time had come to leave. Casablanca was becoming so attractive that every day increased the wrench of departure. On October 5 I took the plane for the Canaries. We landed in Tenerife, and I was soon back in Las Palmas. There another fortnight was taken up by the efforts of friends, nature, sport, and music to detain me.

The music was that of the concerts and the theater, the friendship that of the yachts' crews I remembered so well, of *Maeva* and *Nymph Errant*, which had arrived during my absence. Such is the marvelous fraternity of the sea that I remember one evening in the *Nymph Errant* when the eleven people present were made up of nine nationalities: three Englishmen, an American, an Italian, a Spaniard, a Swiss, a Dane, a Dutchman, a Frenchman, and an Australian girl.

Nature exerted her charm through excursions to Cruz de Tejeda and Agaete in company with my charming guides, Calmano and Collachio, and the sporting attractions included our sessions at the swimming pool, where the adorable lady champion of Spain gave her dazzling exhibitions, and I was beaten in a two-hundred-meter crawl by that dynamic old gentleman, M. Boiteux *Père*.

"Watch out, Alain, if you stay too long, you will never have the strength to leave." This thought used to torment me during long, sleepless nights. But there was nothing to be done, the wind was still in the south. Until it veered, there was no point in starting. Perhaps the new moon would bring some improvement. Finally, on October 18, the wind changed, and I announced that I would leave the next day.

Atlantic Challenge

That Sunday, October 19, the wind finally blew from the right quarter, steadily from the north-northeast. At long last the trade wind had arrived. A French yacht was to tow me out of the harbor. My friends rallied around in a heart-warming fashion, showing a spirit of understanding which touched me to the quick. M. Farnoux, our Consul in Las Palmas, took me to Mass in the morning and then accompanied me to the yacht club. His first intention had been to join the yacht which was going to tow me and say good-by out at sea, but we were both so moved that, fearing possibly to upset me further, he suddenly said in an almost gruff tone:

"No, I'm not coming. Let me embrace you. I shall not be there this afternoon. Please don't think badly of me."

As if I could. I embraced him and we parted. It was Boiteux' father who finally came with me to *L'Hérétique*. My equipment and stores of food, checked and sealed by the consular authorities, were already on board, together with the radio set which I had been given. Angelito, the head pilot, made one last inspection and gave my sextant a final check. While all this was going on, quite a crowd had gathered. I was presented with a gift of the club burgee and asked to sign the golden book. All my friends were there and even strangers went out of their way to show their good will. I was astonished, once we had set off, to find myself at the head of a veritable convoy which accompanied me out of the harbor, with all the ships in the port sounding their sirens. Sailing yachts of every shape and size tacked and crossed all around me, their white sails looking like sea gulls; some of their occupants made the sign of the cross as they passed to bring me luck. We all felt that the supreme test was about to commence.

As if to encourage me on my way, a great three-masted sailing schooner, the cadet training ship of the Spanish navy, was hove to where I decided to cast off my tow. I felt that Fortune, in the guise of this survivor of the days of sail, had contrived this encouraging gesture. There she lay, lifting gently in the swell, one of the last reminders of ghostships, long voyages wracked by scurvy, the castaways of *La Méduse,* of those who had died of hunger and been engulfed in the man-eating sea. I had just cast off my tow when I saw the training ship's flag dip slowly in salute; all the cadets lined along the rail removed their caps as I passed. The thought struck me for a moment that in all the world's navies this was the manner of showing respect to the dead. To show I knew I would win through I hoisted my sail smoothly and slowly drew away from the little yachts still tacking and crossing and saluting either with their flag or their mainsail.

Gradually they were lost from sight, all except the big schooner, which then rendered me the last and most splendid salute. The midshipmen furled and then tautened their three topsails in a whipcrack of wind and canvas which echoed across the water. It sounded more as if they were hailing my triumph rather than honoring my departure.

The evening was completely clear, the wind blow steadily from the north-northeast, and the dinghy forged ahead at a good three and a half knots toward the south of the Grand Canary. I intended to hold a south-southwesterly course before turning due west. My position was exactly on the twenty-eighth degree of latitude north and fifteen degrees of longitude west. My goal in the West Indies lay roughly on the sixtieth degree of longitude west, with several possible landfalls between the twelfth and eighteenth degree of latitude north. I had decided against setting a westerly course straight away in order to avoid the Sargasso Sea, which, with the Doldrums, was one of the two major dangers of which I had to steer clear.

North of the route I had chosen, the Northern Equatorial Current and the Gulf Stream formed between them a gigantic eddy some five thousand miles in circumference, containing a great mass of seaweed, the origin of which has always been a mystery: this is the Sargasso Sea, a great, dead expanse. It is said that no form of edible fish has ever been caught there. The whole area has always been a major navigational hazard; a terrible trap, where plant filaments and seaweed grip vessels in an unbreakable net. To the north it was the sea that spelled danger. To the south the winds were the menace. Here the two powerful trade winds, one blowing from the northeast, out of Portugal, and the other from the southeast, where the Congo lies, meet in a tremendous conflict in a no man's land of violent storms, unpredictable turbulence and disquieting calms, a sort of buffer state between the northern and southern hemispheres. It is called the Doldrums, a region of anarchic violence of the elements which was very nearly fatal to Mermoz, and from which I knew I would not be able to free myself if I were caught there. To my right I was threatened by the currents, to my left by the winds.

The stiff breeze which had sped me on my way did not last for long; it abandoned me during the evening. Looking at my useless sail, I wondered how long the calm would last, having had no previous experience to guide me. Slowly and relentlessly the current carried L'Hérétique to the south. I fixed my lantern to the mast so that I would be seen by the numerous ships which cross between the Grand Canary and Fuerteventura. With my steering oar lashed, the tent cover pulled up to my neck like a blanket, my head on the life belts, I dropped off to sleep about half-past eight. *L'Hérétique* drifted slowly in the dead calm. It was a cool night under a lovely, luminous sky.

The next day, and the day following, there was still no wind and I was in exactly the same position as on the day of my arrival when the mist had hidden the islands. I was completely isolated and knew only that there was one island to the right, another to the left, and that I could not see a thing. I was impatient to get out into the broad Atlantic, where I would no longer need to show a light at night,—where there would be no ships to see me.

Monday had brought the first sign of life in the sea around me. Unfortunately, they were still only small fish which swam ahead of the dinghy like pilots. They were difficult to catch and would have provided me with very little food. I began to fear that the calm would never break, but during the afternoon of the third day, a breeze sprang up and I was able to set course for the twenty-first parallel. I intended to hold this course for about ten days, assuming it would bring me about a hundred miles to the west of the Cape Verde Islands, whence I would head straight for the West Indies. That day I wrote in my journal:

"Morale excellent, but sun hot. Very thirsty. Drank a little sea water as the fish are still sulking; have been able to catch only about three pounds, quite insufficient to provide fresh water. However, this should improve. Water seems much less salty than in the Mediterranean."

That night my situation was really brought home to me. It was all very different from the dummy run I had made across the Mediterranean, a busy, civilized lake, crisscrossed by ships. Now I was in a boundless ocean, with little likelihood of meeting any vessels. The Atlantic would really put my theories to the test.

Right from the start, everything combined to bring this realization home to me.

The trade wind sprang up again. Soon it approached gale strength. Carrying me first on their crests and then in their troughs, the waves either protected me from or exposed me to its blast. Their tops were breaking all around me. I wondered what would happen if *L'Hérétique* came just under one of these onrushing waterfalls.

Unable to do anything about it, but confident in the dinghy's stability, I dropped off to sleep, expecting an untroubled night. It became a nightmare. Suddenly, half in a dream, I seemed to be surrounded by water. Confused and panic-stricken, I tried to gather my thoughts. Was there still a boat under me? Was I in it or in the water? I started swimming, striking out desperately. Half-dead with fright, I woke right up. *L'Hérétique* was completely submerged. I realized that a wave must have broken right on top of me. I must start bailing at once. Only the inflated floats showed above the water. Everything else had become part of the sea, but *L'Hérétique* continued imperturbably on its course. There was no time to give way to despair. Almost instinctively I started scooping out water with my two hands and then with my hat, a ludicrous instrument for what seemed a superhuman task. I had to bail furiously between each big wave so that *L'Hérétique* would survive the next. But even with a proper bailer I would have needed to display a degree of energy which would soon have exhausted me. Every ten or fifteen minutes, a big wave hit the stern board with a thud, and the water flowed in anew, making the previous work useless, pointless, and hopeless. It is still beyond my comprehension how, numbed with cold, I managed to keep this up for two hours. That was the time it took to get the dinghy properly afloat again. I can only say to my fellow castaways: Be more obstinate than the sea. You will win.

I was safe, but everything in the dinghy was soaked with water. When the sun started to dry things out, they would all be covered with a film of salt, which would absorb the humidity every time night fell. The whole craft had become a sort of salt marsh. Most of the equipment was in watertight containers, and fortunately the radio had not been affected. The matches, on the other hand, were absolutely soaked. In due course I spread them out in the boat to dry in the sun, with very little hope of their ever being any use again, but at least I had to try. Fortunately, I had about a hundred boxes with me. I was to be lucky to find one that lighted in every box.

There was still some land in sight. I assumed it was the last I should see. The one great satisfaction I had was that *L'Hérétique* was at least never going to capsize. The dinghy had behaved exactly as I hoped, like an aquaplane or floating platform, sliding over the crests of the waves without offering any resistance. There was a reasonable hope that she would reach the other side in one piece.

The following night, fearing a similar disaster, I lowered the sail as soon as the wind showed signs of freshening. To prevent being flooded by another breaking wave, I put out the sea anchor, thus turning the bow to the swell. But it was exasperating to have to sacrifice the night's run. I had yet to catch a single fish, but the concentric wakes they made around me proved that there were plenty there. As I had foreseen, two days would bring me all I needed.

There is no entry in my log for Thursday, 23. I was too busy all day with needle and thread. The wind had blown up fresh and strong from the right direction: the faithful trade wind from the northeast which was to carry me to my destination. But fate has its own ironies; hardly had I trimmed the sail to the wind when it tore right across at its broadest part. It had brought me all the way from Monaco to the Canaries. When I started off again, I had made up my mind to use it as long as possible and then replace it with the new sail I had in reserve, but I had not expected I would need to change them so soon. I threw out my sea anchor, lowered the sail, and rigged the new one to the yard. Half an hour later a sudden violent gust wrenched it off and sent it flying away like a kite. I saw it splash into the sea a little way off. What was worse, it had carried away the mainsheet and halyards.

I had no alternative but to rely on my old, torn sail, so I started laboriously to sew it together again. All I had was a reel of ordinary black thread and a few darning needles. I had to work on it inch by inch, as the lack of space prevented me from laying the sail out. I had to mend the rent little by little, just as I slowly bailed out the boat. By the time evening came, I had just about finished. I was very tired and preferred not to subject my handiwork to too severe a test. After all, it was the last sail I had, and I could not afford to have it torn away. I had to put out the sea anchor again, and resigned myself to the loss of further precious hours.

During the whole of the rest of the voyage, I always had a pang of fear when I looked at the black darn right across the sail, rather like a piece of scar tissue that threatens to burst. But above all, I was afraid of the very fear it engendered, because increasing tiredness and exhaustion led me to expect the worst, and this in its turn made me weak and cowardly. From this moment on I was prey to an inner conflict of morale, quite as vital as that with the elements. When things were going badly I managed to cope with it, but when there was some slight improvement I would fear the worst again. I began to have doubts about the ability of my equipment to last the course. My low spirits that night are perhaps explained by the fact that I was chattering with cold, soaked to the skin, and encrusted with salt. Never had I waited so desperately for the sun to rise; it seemed that it would be my only salvation. I was to learn, or perhaps I had forgotten, what an unfaithful friend it could be.

I had at this time made very little progress and, what was worse, had very little idea of exactly what distance I had covered. It was the start of my errors in calculating the longitude, which were to have serious consequences. I was still in the area where the trade winds blew strongly. It was only later, when their force was distributed over a larger surface, that they were to diminish in power. For the time being, the waves were the greater menace, tall and whitecapped, like a malicious child showing its pearly teeth. As one does in front of such a child, I tried to hide my fears, and hoisted my patched sail.

I had hardly gathered way again when a harvest of fish arrived. They appeared first as green and blue stains in the water, approaching the dinghy with great suspicion. They disappeared with a flip of their tails as soon as I made any sudden gesture. However, it was high time to start laying in a supply. During the whole day of the twenty-fourth I worked at bending the point of my knife, gently, without breaking it, on the flat part of an oar, as if on an anvil. I then bound the handle of the knife with a length of twine to the end of an oar so that I could harpoon the first fish which came near enough. Almost anything will serve as a lashing —a necktie, shoelace, a belt, or strands of rope; a castaway would always have something of the sort. I intended to dispense as far as possible with my emergency fishing kit. Although this is standard equipment, in a sealed box, of most lifeboats, castaways on a raft might well be without it. I intended to do what I could with the material on board. While I was working away, several birds, to my great astonishment, wheeled overhead. I had been convinced there would be none once I was out of range of land, and thus exploded another landlubbers' myth. Not a single day was to pass without seeing some form of bird life. One in particular became a personal acquaintance. Every day of the voyage, he appeared about four o'clock, to circle a few times over *L'Hérétique*. For the time being, however, I was concentrating on the fish.

On Saturday, 25, after half catching and wounding a number of fish and then seeing them wriggle off the end of my makeshift harpoon, I managed to catch my first dolphin. (Or, to be correct, dorado. These are fish, not mammals, but I shall use their more common name.) I was saved. Not only did I have food and drink, but bait and hook as well. Behind the gill cover, there is a perfect natural bone hook, such as has been found in the tombs of prehistoric men, and which I think I can claim to have adapted to modern use. My first fishing tackle was at hand. From then on I had all the food and liquid I needed every day and was never in danger of starving. That was probably the most heretical aspect of my self-imposed role of castaway.

During these first days, I was not yet completely alone on the sea's expanse. A number of large ships passed me, apparently bound for the Canaries, but not one altered course to assist me. I shall never know whether I was actually sighted, but it is more than likely that someone in a raft is very difficult to see. I was to have more than one proof of this. On the other hand, *L'Hérétique* was surrounded by an absolute shoal of fish, which never abandoned me. Fishermen and experts had prophesied before my departure that once I had left the Canaries I would never catch a thing. Precisely the contrary happened. The green and blue patches I had noticed became the silhouettes of large, familiar fish, jostling around the dinghy. I was to get to know their spiny backs well, recognizing them as old friends. Every now and then a crack like a pistol shot attracted my attention, just in time to see a silvery underside disappearing into the waves.

The wind had now become predictable and regular. I left my sail set night and day, and with no land obstacles to avoid, I was able to run before it without worry, watching the slightly faster swell roll past me. Just as speed assures a cyclist's balance, so it gave me additional security. If I had stopped, the waves would have broken against my stern board and flooded the boat. But I could not help feeling worried about my equipment, particularly the patched sail, wondering whether it would stay the course. I wrote in my log:

"Before I left, I was convinced that my chief anxiety would be to obtain food and drink, but it transpires that the chief worry is about the durability of one's equipment, and the no less serious problem of humidity. I have no option but to continue using the damp clothes I have with me; otherwise the cold would kill me.

And I noted, already at this early stage: "A castaway should never take off his clothes, even if they are wet."

I realized, even though I had been soaked to the skin on the second day, that wet clothes succeed in conserving the body's warmth. I was purposely wearing the sort of clothing that a castaway might have, trousers, shirt, a pull-over, and a jacket. Wiser now from experience, I no longer regarded as figures of fun the mussel and shrimp catchers who always wear the warmest clothing they can get, with long woolen stockings and stout waterproof boots, in spite of the weight involved when trudging through the shallows.

By Sunday, October 26, I had written in my log: "Can no longer determine my longitude with certainty. I shall just have to guess it from the time the sun reaches its meridian."

This problem had acquired grave importance. In principle, the height of the sun above the horizon at noon should enable me to determine my latitude, and the changing time at which it reached its zenith should give me my longitude. When I left I was on the fifteenth degree of longitude; I should have found the sun at the summit of its trajectory at one o'clock by my watch, which was set to GMT. In fact, when I first timed it, the sun reached its zenith at twelve-fifteen. I therefore estimated that I needed to make a correction of forty-five minutes, an error which was to lead me into others still greater.

That day I found in my pocket, among many unread letters which had been delivered during the commotion surrounding our departure, a note from my friend John Staniland, owner of the yacht *Nymph Errant,* who was due to leave the Canaries three weeks after myself. It gave the address to which he had asked me to telegraph news of my arrival in the West Indies: "John Staniland, % King's Harbor Master, Bridgetown, Barbados, to await arrival of British yacht." He must have known that he would get there long before me but clearly wanted to encourage me by suggesting that I would get there first.

I was still overoptimistic. I wrote in my log: "If I am where I think I am, I should be at Latitude 21° North by Wednesday, changing course to the west on Thursday, after covering seven hundred miles in ten days. This should leave me eighteen hundred to go, another twenty-five days at my present speed. However, I must not be too optimistic."

The main thing was to be of good heart, and I was full of hope during most of the crossing. It seemed as if I had only left the night before, although I had already been at sea a week. Now that I am back, I am often asked if I was not bored. That at least is something that never happens at sea. This adventure formed a separate compartment in my life. Although each day seemed interminable, time had lost all relative importance. There were no points of reference on which to base its passage, such as appointments, the day's normal rigid timetable. Time passed without my being aware of it. Only later, when this existence had acquired a semblance of normality, and I was able to compare a particular day with others exactly like it, did time begin to weigh heavily.

The second week brought an anniversary which made me a little homesick. It was my birthday. After I arrived in Barbados, and people asked how old I was, I used to reply: "I was twenty-eight at sea."

My luck held that day and gave me a sort of birthday present. My homemade fishing tackle, the hook baited with a piece of flying fish, was trailing in the wake when a big bird, which in English is called a shearwater, and for which I have yet to find any French equivalent, pounced on the bait. I pulled it slowly inboard. I was a little worried that he might peck holes in my inflated rubber floats, but no sooner did I have him in the dinghy than he seemed to have an attack of seasickness, vomiting all over the deck. The creature was only half-conscious, and with a slight feeling of repugnance, I wrung its neck.

I had never eaten raw bird meat in my life, but after all, considering that steak tartare is a delicacy, why not the flesh of a bird? My strong advice to those who catch a sea bird is not to pluck it, but to skin it, as the skin is very rich in fat. I cut my shearwater in two, ate one half immediately, and left the other to dry in the sun for the next day. But I was soon disillusioned if I thought my birthday dinner was going to give me a respite from my imposed diet. The flesh was excellent, but it had an undeniable aftertaste of fish.

During the night I received something of a shock. Through my tent I noticed a curious light. At first I thought I had somehow caught fire, but it was only my half of shearwater giving out a strong phosphorescent light, so strong that it was reflected on the sail, giving it quite a ghostly appearance.

October 28 brought an event which was to have dire consequences, although I did not realize it at the time. I broke the strap of my watch, one of those self-winding models actuated by movements of the wrist. I fixed it to the front of my sweater with a pin, assuming that my movements would keep it going, but in the cramped interior of the dinghy, they were to prove insufficient. It stopped soon afterward, and it was too late to set it again. It became impossible to determine with any certainty what progress I was making to the west, the direction of the islands where I hoped to land. After my watch, and later, my radio, had failed me, the times entered in my log were based on guesswork. This incident brought home to me how much the aimlessness of doing what I pleased, of not deciding in advance how to fill my day, could undermine me, and I decided to work out a strict timetable of activity. I am convinced that in such circumstances it is essential for the castaway to remain master of events, rather than be content merely to react to them. In order to get away from the constant and unrelieved proximity of the sea, I decided to adopt the peasants' habit of getting up and going to bed with the sun.

At dawn I collected the flying fish, which crashed unsuspectingly into the sail during the night and fell on the top of the tent. I had collected the first on the third day out and during the rest of the voyage picked up between five and fifteen every morning. I ate the two largest for my breakfast. Then I fished for an hour, catching more than enough food for the day. I divided my haul into two parts, one for lunch and one for dinner. Why did I not change my meal hours, it may be asked, instead of eating at the accepted times of morning, noon, and evening? I felt that having already altered so radically the nature of my food, it would only place an additional strain on my stomach to change its working hours. It had acquired the habit of secreting certain gastric juices at certain times in order to digest the food it received, and I saw no point in disrupting its functions further.

After the hour's fishing, I devoted the same amount of time to a minute inspection of the boat; the smallest area of friction could have proved fatal. The back of a book, the deck boards, even the radio, rubbing gently on one spot would have sufficed to wear a hole in the rubber floats in a few days. Those who now visit *L'Hérétique* in the Naval Museum in Paris will note that, despite all my precautions, there is quite a worn surface on the right-hand side, where I used to rest my back. At the end of forty-eight hours I noticed with a shock that the mere fact of leaning against the inner wall had been sufficient to rub off the paint. I had to find something to put between myself and the float to prevent further friction. Once the paint had gone I would start wearing away the rubberized canvas, rendering it no longer watertight. I put my ear to the floats to see if I could hear any sign of rubbing, much as I would have done in sounding someone's chest cavity with a stethoscope. I carried out this inspection every day. Like a human lung, the air-filled float transmitted and amplified noises. The faintest sound would have enabled me to track down a puncture. I took a further precaution. There was clearly going to be a gradual loss of pressure in each section of the floats, not necessarily identical. At night I therefore closed the valves between the sections, leaving them open during the day. If one of the sections had lost more air than the other, there would have been a whistle as air passed through the valve to compensate the pressure when I turned the cock each morning. Thank God this was something that never happened. But the detailed morning inspection, running my fingers over the whole surface, combined with the sounding, several times saved me from catastrophe. Every castaway should regard this tireless vigilance as an absolute necessity.

I then did half an hour's exercises to tone up my muscles and keep myself supple, after which I caught the two coffee cups or so of plankton I needed to keep scurvy at bay. This, I figured, took me between ten and twenty minutes. The trouble was that any net trailed from the boat acted as a brake, and I had to make up my mind whether to catch just a little plankton and keep up my speed, or gather enough to serve as food and reduce the day's run. I therefore decided that as long as there was plenty of fish I would treat the plankton as a sort of medicine for supplying me with vitamin C content.

Noon was the time for taking my position. To make quite sure of getting a good sight, I spent half an hour beforehand practicing with the sextant, as the dinghy was always very unsteady. As the sun rose to its zenith, the increase in the angle got smaller and smaller, until it appeared to remain steady. That was the crucial moment. In spite of the great difficulties caused by my lack of elevation above the surface of the water, which resulted in a horizon that was frequently obscured, I soon became very adept at this little game. The mistake to avoid was that of taking the crest of a wave for the true horizon. The swell was strong but regular, as there was no near-by coast to modify its pattern. I had discovered it had rhythm in which every sixth or seventh wave was higher than the others, and its summit gave me a clear view of the horizon. Focusing through the eyepiece of the sextant, I used to count the waves without looking at them, and on the seventh took the bearing. At that second I had to coincide the lower rim of the sun with the line of the horizon by adjusting the arm of the sextant so that they appeared in the eyepiece in exact juxtaposition. Although I had been anything up to ten miles out in my calculations at the beginning of the voyage, by the end of a week I was determining my latitude within a mile or so.

The afternoon was the longest and most difficult part of the day, with no way of hiding from the pitiless sun. I devoted the time to reading, writing, and my medical studies. At two o'clock I gave myself a complete physical check-up: blood pressure, temperature, state of the skin, nails, and hair, condition of the mucous membranes, noting the sea and air temperatures, humidity, and weather conditions. Then I subjected myself to a sort of examination of my state of mind and morale and tried to exercise my memory, after which I read the books and music scores I had with me and did regular translation work.

When the sun passed behind my sail, giving me some respite from its rays, I carried out my evening medical examination: measurement of urine, muscular strength, stools passed, plus a résumé of the day's activities: the day's haul of fish, its quantity and quality and the use I had made of it, a note of the day's plankton catch, its nature, quantity, and taste, and a description of the sea birds I had seen. I allowed myself the luxury of an hour or two listening to the radio after the evening meal. Dusk brought the night's sleep.

During the course of the voyage, one problem became increasingly insistent: to know where to put myself, as a sitting position had already become uncomfortable. I used to sit either on the floats with my legs hanging down, or on the deck boards, my back resting against one float and my legs on the other. In the first position, my legs grew heavy and I ran the risk of edema of the ankles; and in the second, not only did my raised legs start to ache, but they had to lie across the oars, which bit into them and forced me to change my position continually. Sometimes I stretched out on the planks, but as I was starting to lose weight, my bones began to ache from the hard surface, and I could not maintain the position for long. It was practically impossible to stand upright; the best that I could manage was to squat on half-flexed knees, balancing against one of the floats in moody contemplation of the sea. As an additional security precaution I had fastened a line about twenty-five yards long around my waist, with the end attached to the base of the mast. The dinghy was remarkably stable, but I had only to change position for it to rock and I always needed to hold on to something. Fortunately, it neither pitched nor rolled. Nevertheless, I always had the feeling that a single wave could put an end to the whole expedition. All around me, giant waves were breaking with a noise like thunder. Any one of them breaking over the dinghy could have made short shrift of both the experiment and my life.

On October 28 I noted: "I am not dreaming about food; a good sign." Indeed, it was the best proof that I was not hungry, because hunger is above all an obsession. I had no cravings of any sort.

The next day I was suddenly overwhelmed by the thought of the tragic situation I was in. Apart from its length, this part of my voyage had an inevitable quality absent from the previous legs. It was impossible for me to stop or turn around; there was not the slightest possibility of any help. I was just a drop in the ocean, part of a world not to be measured in human terms. I often had cold shivers down my spine. I had not sighted a ship for some time. The previous day I had seen my first shark since leaving the Canaries, but it passed quickly by. The dolphins, on the other hand, had become familiar acquaintances. I even talked to them at times, as the only friends in sight. When I woke up during the night, I was always struck by the beauty of these creatures, swimming alongside me and leaving phosphorescent wakes like shooting stars.

From sheer curiosity I thought I would see what effect the beam of an electric torch would have. As soon as I switched it on, all the fish concentrated in its circle of light. I was still lost in admiration of their intricate evolutions, which I could direct more or less at will, when a sudden buffet forced me to clutch the side of the boat. It was a large shark, the upper part of its tail much longer than the lower. It had turned over on its back to swim toward me. All its teeth and its pure white underside flashed in the light of the torch. It butted its snout repeatedly on the side of the dinghy. Whether it was trying to take a good bite I do not know, but I had always heard that sharks turned on their backs to seize their prey. I was petrified with fear. The only shark I had seen up till then, between Casablanca and the Canaries, had followed me at a respectful distance, but this one had probably lived too far out to sea to learn such civilized behavior. I snapped out the light in the hope that it would go away. For a moment or two its tail continued to beat around me like the cracks of a whip, splashing me with sea water from head to foot. Its white stomach appeared from time to time amidst the phosphorescence, but then, presumably bored by my inactivity, it made off. It is more than likely that the attack was serious, but I comforted myself with the thought of how difficult it must be to bite a football. This somewhat reassured me, but I hoped that in the future such undesirable guests would keep their distance. I had also learned my lesson and never again flashed my torch on the sea. From that day, encouraged by the complete absence of any sea traffic, I also decided to save paraffin by no longer showing a navigation light. My morale was still high, although I was beginning to suffer from the cold at night, the effects of immobility and the consequences of never being dry, due to the humidity.

I was beginning to show the first physical effects of my ordeal. I noted in my logbook:

"Have lost the nail on the small toe of my right foot, and there is a strange rash, probably due to the salt, on the backs of my hands. Afraid of getting boils, which I know will be terribly painful, and which I would try not to treat in order to give no false values to the experiment. I have a few antibiotics on board, but if I use them, future castaways may object that they had no medicaments. Have made up my mind only to use them as a last resort."

I was also experiencing the first general effects of solitude and fatigue, and found myself comparing my situation with a more normal existence: "Am paying a heavy price for all the pleasant days I have spent on land," I noted and, still the optimist, calculated that I only had between twenty-five and forty days to go.

In retrospect, it is amusing (although at the time it was more tragic) to see how the route I marked on my chart acquired the significance of a land journey:

"On reaching latitude 21° North, I shall turn right, steering 255° instead of 230°." Even the figures began to read like highway numbers, and I really felt at the time that my next move was to take the first turning to the right. I began to endow the limitless expanse of the ocean with the characteristics of a familiar city.

"In writing up the log, I have missed taking my latitude; no matter, I can do it tomorrow. There is plenty of time. After all, Columbus took twenty-two days at this time of year for the same voyage; I am expecting to do it in thirty-five or forty. I must learn to vegetate and live the contemplative life; if I think too much, the day seems to last longer."

The next entry asked a question: "I wonder if things would be easier if I were not alone. I really think so. Why is Jack not here? Well, it is no good thinking about it. My God, this trade wind is strong. As long as the sail holds out, so much the better. I shall get there more quickly, but I am absolutely soaked."

Thursday, the thirtieth, was a day of delirious optimism. The entry reads: "Another twenty-three days" (which would have meant my arrival on November 23); but I added as a rider: "Providing all goes well."

This optimism may seem surprising and sound more like a remark made after the event, especially in view of the possible duration of the voyage I had already calculated. But I had always borne in mind the necessity of making a generous allowance to calm the fears of those at home. When I said: "I shall need thirty-five days" rather than sixty, it was because I felt that twenty days might see it through, rather than the verbal estimate.

"A beautiful day and night, calm and without incident. I dreamed about my library of phonograph records. A plane passed right above me, certainly without seeing me. Slightest friction still a serious menace."

This last remark referred to the tiny inflatable emergency dinghy which I kept in the bow of the boat so that I could blow it up rapidly and launch it in the event of some accident. During the night, one of the guy ropes of the mast had rubbed constantly against it, making a neat little round hole. It was a severe shock to learn that only one night of friction by some quite light body was sufficient to puncture the rubberized tissue. In case of any accident to *L'Hérétique,* I no longer had anything to keep me afloat. It is true that my chances of survival in the emergency dinghy would have been extremely small. It was a small, one-man float designed to save people in difficulties near the beach; I can hardly believe it would have got me across the Atlantic. However, the puncture deprived me of the pleasure of launching it at the end of a line so that I could photograph *L'Hérétique* forging ahead in the middle of the Atlantic under full sail. In fact, circumstances were reducing me more and more to the condition of a real castaway. The craft I was in was really my last chance.

"Am counting up the days too often and it only seems to make the time pass more slowly. My catch of fish is diminishing in number but increasing in weight; can now drink from the fish daily by cutting slits in the flesh, without having to cut them into pieces and use the press. No longer need to keep any pieces in my shirt to dry for further use. What a superb day! Fresh trade wind starting to fall off somewhat; it is now a strong breeze, but still from the right direction. As far as I can make out, I am at about 21° 28′ North, more or less in the estimated time."

I was to learn later that I was only at about Longitude 18° or 19°. I was convinced at the time that I still only had to make 35° to the west and 4° to the south, that is to say, some eighteen hundred or nineteen hundred miles, and I was sure I had already covered a quarter of my route. My true position will be appreciated in due course. The entry for Friday, October 31, was as follows:

"Wind freshened a little during the night. Making good speed. A superb shearwater flew over, and I tried to catch it, thinking nostalgically of the bird on my birthday. But this one refuses to co-operate."

The previous evening had been splendid, and I listened to Schubert's lovely *Seventh Symphony*. It almost became the signature tune of the voyage. Although it is not played often, I heard it six times during the sixty-five days I was at sea.

I was still bursting with optimism and noted the same day: "Should sight land from Saturday, November 22." I was in fact destined to see it and land on December 23, a whole month later. I already seemed to be having doubts about my navigation, as I noted at four o'clock:

"Navigation is by no means a simple affair. There is all this business of declination to be taken into account, but my Atlantic route chart does not give it. The problem is to know whether the compass course is a true one, what headway I have made to the west, or whether the westward declination has altered. Otherwise I am much farther south than I think. The change in my latitude should have confirmed this, but my true speed is so difficult to measure that it is almost impossible to navigate by dead reckoning. Assume that I am making eighty miles a day. [An estimate which time was to prove stupidly optimistic.] Should do better still. [Even more crazy.] The most important thing is to remain between the seventeenth and eighteenth degrees of latitude north. Tomorrow, if I am on the right course, I should about be on 20° 20′ North. The trade wind is marvelous. Longitude is about 26° 40′. [That was the real error. I was still about on the eighteenth degree.] Which leaves about 33° to go west, roughly seventeen hundred miles, say twenty-two or twenty-three days at eighty miles a day."

Then I added: "If the wind holds, that must be the pattern of it; surely I must know as much about navigation as Christopher Columbus." The solitude must have started to affect me the day I wrote that. I had begun to understand the difference between solitude and isolation. Moments of isolation in ordinary life can soon be ended; it is just a question of going out of the door into the street or dialing a number on the telephone to hear the voice of a friend. Isolation is merely a matter of isolating oneself, but total solitude is an oppressive thing and slowly wears down its lonely victim. It seemed sometimes as if the immense and absolute solitude of the ocean's expanse were concentrated right on top of me, as if my beating heart were the center of gravity of a mass which was at the same time nothingness. The day I dropped the tow off Las Palmas I thought that solitude was something I would be able to master, once I had become accustomed to its presence. I had been too presumptuous. It was not something I had carried with me; it could not be measured by the confines of myself or the boat. It was a vast presence which engulfed me. Its spell could not be broken, any more than the horizon was finite. And if from time to time I talked aloud in order to hear my own voice, I felt even more alone, a hostage to silence.

On November 1, I reached Latitude 20° North and turned

right. My course was now west, still a few degrees to the south but very little. I had to try to cover the degrees of longitude and put the dinghy on the opposite tack, that is to say, the sail had swung from the right side of the boat to the left and in the normal course should have stayed in that position without being touched until my arrival. In fact I was no longer steering the boat at all; I had lashed the rudder so that the dinghy followed the compass course.

Every two hours or so, I checked the course and occasionally made some small adjustment to the rudder position. The night was spent in a constant condition of dampness, even when the day had been fine and sunny. Despite this, I usually slept for about twelve hours. It may cause surprise that I was able to rest for so long in such circumstances. It was largely a question of confidence. I was satisfied that the dinghy would stay above the waves which battered it from all sides. I realized that if a wave should break inboard, the situation would be desperate, but that the dinghy was unlikely to capsize. My reasoning was based on the comforting if somewhat naïve notion that if nothing happened during the day, I had nothing to fear during the night.

I had nothing to protect my head, as I pulled up the tent only as far as my neck, like a blanket, leaving my face open to a starlit sky such as I have never seen before or since. The light of the moon did duty as a friendly night watchman's lamp.

The trade wind continued steady. I did not dare read too much for fear of having no way to occupy my time once I had run through my stock of books, which was already getting low. Although I continued to ship a little water from time to time, my things started to dry out somewhat. I took advantage of the better conditions to start my calculations again. Every day seemed to tell the same optimistic story: You will land about the twenty-third; you will land about the twenty-third; you will land about the twenty-third. I estimated my longitude at about 27° 30′. There seemed to be many less birds and not quite as many fish. It was now taking me two or two and a half hours a day to catch the necessary amount. There was still no sign of any floating seaweed, but then I was aiming to pass well to the south of the Sargasso Sea. It was clear that I was still drifting to the south, as the signals from Dakar radio station gradually increased in strength. I was also making headway to the west, as I was starting to pick up some of the American stations. But the air waves over the Atlantic were monopolized by two nations: Britain and Russia.

Sunday, November 2, will remain in my memory because I did a very stupid thing. For some days my health had not been so good. The change of food and the constant humidity had caused a general skin eruption of painful little spots. I hoped to prevent their forming scabs by resting my weight on a little pneumatic cushion, the only one I had. Some clumsy movement must have knocked it overboard, a fact I realized only when I saw it floating a couple of hundred yards or so astern. I lowered the sail, put out the sea anchor, and dived in to fetch it. I am a strong swimmer and reached the cushion in a few minutes. Imagine my horror, when I turned around, to see the dinghy sailing off without me, too fast for me to be able to catch it. The sea anchor, normally shaped like a parachute, had fouled itself and was no longer arresting the drift. It was quite clear that I would become exhausted long before I could overhaul it. At that moment *L'Hérétique* very nearly continued the voyage without me.

When I was training to swim the English Channel in 1951, in top physical condition, I once swam for twenty-one hours. Weakened as I was by privation and lack of exercise, I could not possibly have equaled the feat. I abandoned the cushion to its fate and concentrated on the fastest crawl of my life. Even in my race at Las Palmas with the elder Boiteux, I am sure I never attained the same speed. I managed to cut down the distance a little, but then had difficulty even in maintaining it. Suddenly I saw *L'Hérétique* slow down. I caught it up and just managed to hoist myself on board. By a miracle, the cords of the sea anchor had disentangled themselves in the nick of time. I was physically and morally exhausted and swore it was the last dip I would take on the journey.

Relations with my marine neighbors assumed a definite pattern. They became almost like family friends. There were five or six dolphins and a petrel, which paid me a flying visit every day at four o'clock. It was a little black bird, its tail feathers tipped with white, about as large as a Paris sparrow. It baffled me how it had managed to cover such distances to seek its sustenance in the middle of the ocean. It approached from astern every day, sometimes settled down on the sea after four little steps on the water, and disappeared the moment the sun set. The dolphins were much more faithful and stayed with me twenty-four hours a day. They were quite easy to recognize. In trying to catch them with my bent knife the first day, I had wounded them, and the marks still showed. I noted with interest that fish, like human beings, seem to heal slowly in sea water. One of my dolphins had an open place about the size of a half crown toward the end of its back, and another had been hurt on one of its fins. There were five or six I recognized in the same manner, and I gave them all names. The largest one I called "Dora." She never left me, but took good care not to come near enough for a second thrust. She cast a fishy eye in my direction whenever she came near enough to the boat and sometimes turned on her side to look at the sky. When the wind was light and my speed dropped, they used to take quick runs at the dinghy and smack the floats with their tails, as if to ask why I was lagging. They were joined regularly by newcomers, and these were the ones I managed to catch. All I needed was my bone hook, fixed to a length of string, baited with the flying fish I picked up every morning on my tent. I pulled the bait rapidly across the surface of the water, as if it were a flying fish skidding over the surface before diving again. The dolphins fairly fought for it, like dogs for a bone, and one of them usually took the hook. All the new arrivals fell for this trick, but my old friends, knowing me too well, never as much as moved from their tracks.

During the night of November 3, I caught a long, thin, villainous-looking fish. It had a mouthful of vicious teeth which made a noise like a firecracker. In spite of the fight it had put up in the water, it seemed to go dead, strangely enough, after one final contortion, the moment I pulled it aboard. I assumed it was a fish normally inhabiting great depths. Its eyes were huge in proportion to its head, and its teeth enormous. I completely failed to identify it. In view of its menacing copper color, the poisonous look of the whitish slime its mouth was dripping on my sleeping bag, where it had landed, I picked it up by the tail with immense care and threw it back in the water.

I learned later that it was a gempylus, the same sort of snake mackerel which landed on the sleeping bag of one of the members of the crew of the *Kon-Tiki*. The beast must have a particular affinity for sleeping bags. Mine also got a good bite that night. I used it with a certain amount of care from then on, thinking with some trepidation of the organic poisons used by South American Indians to treat their arrows.

At eleven o'clock the next morning, a ship passed about a dozen miles away without seeing me. "Pity the poor castaway," I noted. "He can count on no one but himself. I was between the ship and the sun and was not sighted. Even so the vessel stopped for a good ten minutes to take its position. I wish it had sighted me, as I could have sent a reassuring message to my family. Its course was to the northeast, presumably on the route from America to the Azores." (It must be remembered that I thought myself much farther west than I was. The ship was probably on its way from the Cape Verde Islands to the Canaries.)

If only I had known what the future held for me! A new error had started to creep into the calculations of my position. The *Pilot Book* gave me the hour of sunset for my latitude on the meridian of Greenwich. In theory I should have added four

minutes for every degree of longitude, and the same was nom-
inally true for the duration of the moon's rise and set. Now,
although my estimated longitude did not correspond at all with the
longitude given by the sun at midday and when it set, it did coincide exactly with that given by the time of the setting of the
moon. I was quite incapable of explaining this discrepancy, and
only learned the secret later from a French naval officer. It seems
there is a problem of refraction involved.

I started to pass the time with little private parlor games, particularly with memory tests. Although I had never been a lover
of arithmetic, I started to do immensely complicated sums in my
head, dividing the twenty-seven hundred miles of my voyage
by the number of miles I estimated for the day's run, in order
to calculate how many days were left, and this I did half a dozen
times or more, each with a different divisor.

To add to the turmoil in my head, I became very superstitious
about small things, the inevitable accompaniment of solitude. If
I could not find my pipe the moment I looked for it, I considered
it a bad omen. The little doll mascot, which my friends had given
me on leaving the Canaries, began to acquire a tangible per-
sonality. I used to look at her and start a conversation, first of all
in monosyllables, then whole sentences, describing exactly the
next thing I was going to do. I did not wait for a reply. It was
not yet a dialogue, although that would come. For the time being
I just needed to assert myself. My dwindling stock of damp cigarettes created another superstition. Now and again I would try
to light one. The number of matches I had to strike came to rep-
resent the number of days I would need to complete the voyage.
Taking as point of departure the fact that I could not possibly
arrive before November 23, I used to count as follows: if the
first match caught, I would arrive on the twenty-third; the second
meant arriving between the twenty-third and the twenty-fifth,
and so on. You can see how far a box would lead, and if it took
too long, I used to discount the evidence, as I was still an op-

timist; that is to say, I accepted all the good auguries and ignored all the bad ones. It is not a bad basis for contentment.

I began to know the exact sound of everything on board when sailing at normal speeds. When the wind was moderate, I used to estimate my speed by the exact note of the sail's song. Although the wind had dropped for a couple of days, it freshened again, and I appeared to be making about four knots. If only I could keep it up I would be there in twenty days. . . .

"Tuesday, November 4. The moon sight gave me nine degrees of difference from that of the sun and three degrees from my estimated position. I am completely baffled. My radio is working less well, and I can hear it only during the evening hours, when conditions are most favorable. I still take my estimated position as a basis, with that given by the moon as an optimistic possibility. Still steering due west; calculate I am on latitude 18° 58′ North. Five months ago we were in sight of Minorca, where we were to land the next day at the end of our first lap. It seems a long time ago. By 1800 hours had caught no fish, particularly exasperating as I am surrounded by pilot fish. By 1900 hours had caught my dinner; at least I shall not have to fast during the night. Visited by a magnificent white sea gull and surrounded by porpoises. Weather perfect, with the wind driving *L'Hérétique* along at maximum speed with no waves breaking inboard. If only this lasts."

My urine was still perfectly normal and my general health seemed good. Nevertheless, looking back on my last week on land, the comparison seemed odious, but there were plenty of days to come which would appear much worse.

The voyage was more difficult and certainly more tedious than I had expected. However, at the end of twelve more days I expected to change the chart and start using that for the Caribbean approaches. That would mean I had eight hundred miles to go. The voyage from Casablanca to Las Palmas began to seem like child's play. I had finally given up any idea of showing a light at night. I may have missed thereby an occasion of sending news by a passing ship, and this began to weigh on me. I had lost the taste for reading. I should have paid more attention before leaving to the old problem of what books to take on a desert island. In order to have a little of everything, I had brought with me some Molière and a complete Rabelais, a Cervantes, a Nietzsche, Aeschylus in the two languages, Spinoza, a selection from Montaigne, and, as musical scores, the two Passions of Bach and the Quartets of Beethoven.

"I have no fear of a collision, the sea is absolutely empty. I will start showing a light at about 50° West, that is to say, in about twelve days (*sic*), unless there is an increase in traffic before then."

On Wednesday, November 5, I invented a new superstition, meditating profoundly on the significance of Wednesdays in my voyage.

"*Eighteenth day:* Wednesdays have acquired a curious importance (or at least so I believe). I am sure that I shall arrive on a Wednesday.

"Wednesday, June 11 first lap to Ciudadela.

"Wednesday, June 18, returned to Ciudadela after the capsize.

"Wednesday, July 9, landing on Ibiza beach.

"Wednesday, July 16, entered harbor of Ibiza.

"Wednesday, July 23, entered Motril harbor.

"Wednesday, August 13, left Tangier alone.

"Wednesday, August 20, arrived at Casablanca.

"Wednesday, September 3, arrived in the Canaries.

"Wednesday, September 10, Nathalie's birth announced.

"Wednesday, September 24, arrived at Casablanca from Paris.

"Wednesday, October 1, presented with my radio.

"And Wednesday, November 5, halfway between Casablanca and the West Indies."

I was being visited more frequently by sharks, but I had become quite used to them and treated them with complete disdain. They seemed a cowardly lot. A smart rap on the snout, and they were off like a flash. They often came to prod the floats with their noses, so I usually picked up an oar and clouted them on the head. They never waited for more and immediately plunged out of sight. My dolphins must have been highly amused as they usually did a prudent disappearing act whenever there were sharks around. I must have gone up in their estimation, as their numbers around *L'Hérétique* continually increased. But although they remained completely faithful, the pilot fish abandoned me when I met my first boat, the *Arakaka*. Always opportunists, they preferred the company of the strong.

That Wednesday, November 5, I witnessed a fairylike spectacle. I had already seen a number of shoals of flying fish. Most of the time they did one glide over the surface of the sea, but when they were being attacked by the dolphins, they often took off again from the crest of a wave. Using their tails to pick up speed, they literally beat their fins to become air-borne again in order to get away from their pursuers. However, the dolphins usually outwitted them. Skimming along with their dorsal fins breaking the surface, they usually managed to be on the spot where the flying fish touched the water again, and the wretched creatures usually found a large open mouth waiting for them instead of a clear patch of sea.

That day the scene was even more remarkable. Great shoals of flying fish were being attacked by a flock of shearwaters. I was mystified as to how there could be eleven shearwaters circling around me at such a distance from the coast. What I did not know was that I was at that moment almost within sight of the Cape Verde Islands.

All would have been well if my buttocks had not started to feel sore. I was afraid I might be developing boils. I also had a slight attack of parotitis, or inflammation of the salivary glands, of which the more severe and infectious form is mumps. However, I was still full of hope, and after four days I was able to note: "Should arrive next week. Things could be worse, but I am starting to become obsessed with the idea of food. Promise myself an absolute feast of fruit when I arrive. Am getting tired of fish and birds."

The castaway is always told that if birds appear in large numbers, land must be near. In my case this was perfectly true. Land was only about sixty miles away, although it would have been quite impossible for me to head for it in view of the prevailing wind and current. Another proverb of the sea is that land lies in the direction toward which the birds fly. The trouble was that when they left me, they flew off to the west, where there was, in fact, no land for fifteen hundred miles, and not to the southeast, where the Cape Verde Islands lay. It seemed an unkind way of nourishing my hopes.

My next entry read:

"Very hot; oh! for a good pint of beer. My worst privation is undoubtedly the lack of real fresh water. I am sick of eating raw fish, but even more tired of drinking its juice. If only it would rain for a change. There are plenty of clouds in the sky, and the sea is often rough, but there is no sign of rain. I have yet to see a drop."

As a matter of fact, I was not thirsty, I just wanted a decent drink for a change, rather like the man who lost his appetite for macaroni but happily wolfed chicken. I had a nagging desire for fresh water, but it was not a question of physical suffering.

During the night of Thursday, November 6, I was attacked again by a shark. He seemed to be a particularly tough customer and I could not keep him off. He must have acquired a taste for human flesh. I fixed my knife to the end of an oar while he butted away at the floats. I got ready to defend myself, and the next time he turned on his back to attack at an angle I stuck the knife in him and slit him from throat to tail. The sea turned a blackish color around him, and I saw his entrails spilling out. My dolphins pounced on them. They always seemed hungry. For once, the hunter had become the hunted.

The fish must have found the dinghy an original and useful companion, as I was now surrounded by a veritable aquarium. I had never seen so many fish in all my life, even in the aquarium tanks at Monaco. As for those who predicted that I would never catch a thing, I hope their faces are red. Unfortunately, my diet was giving me a mild form of diarrhea. It certainly did not come from drinking sea water, as it was some time since I had found this necessary.

I was writing up my log, when another shark appeared, an absolute monster. It must have been nearly fifteen feet long. I grabbed my camera and started to turn the handle. It was a formidable-looking beast, with a blunt snout and a huge mouth, and looked absolutely ferocious. I closed the valves between my floats as an emergency precaution. If it had managed to bite a chunk out of one of them, I would have to rely on the remaining four. But these beasts, cowards by nature, are much less aggressive during the day than at night. This one came to inspect my rudder oar and swam around me a few times, but otherwise kept his distance. I gave myself a figurative slap for my stupidity in diving after my pneumatic cushion a few days earlier. If a beast like this had attacked me, it would have been the end of the story.

I could still hear the radio at night, but it had become little more than a whisper, and half the time I had to put my ear to the loud-speaker. I could no longer make any check on the time in order to plot my position, and I had not learned to make use of the Pole Star. In any case, the sea water had started to blur the mirrors in my sextant, and the Pole Star was not bright enough to show in it. I was now completely out of touch with the land and deprived of news. I even started to forget what a human voice sounded like. The only voice and tangible presence left was my own, and my life started to resemble more and more that of the animals around me. I began to share their sensations and reactions, eating the same food and catching the same flying fish.

My little petrel still kept up his four o'clock rendezvous, while the dolphins had become my protégés. We all tried to hide from the same sun, they in the shadow cast by the dinghy, and I behind the sail during the afternoon. Like the fish, my point of reference became the wave, instead of the familiar path or row of trees by which the landsman finds his way.

It became almost impossible to realize that there were people on land living a regular life, attaching importance to such things as the clothes they wore. Under the broiling sun, the day more or less passed me by. I had returned to the primitive life. But I still feel a tingle in the spine on reading through my log, especially at the point where I was clearly starting to lose strength. I could see the change in my handwriting. The solitude was becoming increasingly oppressive and the log was my substitute for a human companion. Where I had filled a page or a page and a half each day at the beginning of the journey, I now scribbled two or even three and a half. I wrote little but often, but I was worried that I might run out of paper. When it was necessary to sacrifice a book for purposes of my natural functions, I finally decided that the most appropriate was the Rabelais.

"*Friday, November 7.* Twentieth day. The matches from the Canaries now refuse to light. Fortunately, I still have a few boxes made in Morocco, and these still seem to work even when soaked in sea water and dried in the sun. But I shall have to go carefully with them.

"Calm night, regular wind. I slept well. Staying awake to check the time of moonrise, I was overcome by the feeling of what a strange and formidable element the sea is. It seems to form part of a system so entirely different from normal existence that it might belong to another planet. But there it is at my feet, alive yet inscrutable.

"Here and there lights appear in the depths, signs of a life only to be guessed at, but which seems intense. They look like stars half hidden in a cloudy night sky. The fish around me leap and swim to and fro, protagonists of an unseen and mysterious existence. Life at the surface is only the thin upper layer of another world.

"*Twenty-first day.* A little bubble of water appeared on one of the floats this morning, revealing a tiny air leak. I had a box of rubber patches, but the glue did not seem to hold. I used as substitute a substance of a more physiological nature. I hope I can spare the details by referring to the use to which I was putting my Rabelais. As long as it holds, I am all right."

Early morning and evening brought me a splendid catch of fish. I wondered how the experts would feel. How does one become an expert without any practical experience of a problem? Doubtless by extrapolation, but it is not a scientific method.

The clouds were thickening, and I undressed in their pleasant shade. I examined my various small rashes, caused, I assumed, by perspiration, but my extremities were in good order and my physiological functions perfectly normal. I had grown the most tremendous beard.

"Ginette, my dear, I hope all this will be over soon. But still no ship in sight."

That day I read the following in an article on swordfish in my small encyclopedia of fish: "The redoubtable adversary and scourge of the octopus; normally uses its sword to slash and not to spear, as might be supposed, but when in a blind rage, as is sometimes the case, will attack ships with the point." Hardly reassuring! I could only hope there was little likelihood of meeting one.

I began to think my compass was playing tricks on me. My nominal course was 290/280°, but the true course seemed to be about 260°, unless I was making much greater headway than I thought, and that I preferred to doubt. I expected soon to be on Latitude 17° North (I was on the parallel 17° 30′) and intended to try to remain on it. I was particularly anxious to avoid the

Doldrums, especially when I was only a hundred miles or so from the coast. The sea continued to show inexplicable moods. Usually the swell was slow and regular, but for no apparent reason and with no increase in the force of the wind, it would suddenly become choppy and irregular. I had to watch the boat carefully. My dolphins were still with me and I was catching plenty of fish.

Time was beginning to weigh heavily, and I counted blindly and unhesitatingly on arriving during the week of November 23–30. It never entered my head that December would find me still at sea.

On Saturday, November 8, I noted at dawn "large flock of birds," in spite of being, as I thought, a thousand miles from the nearest land. A large number of flying fish, about the size of large sardines, landed in the dinghy; how delicious they would have tasted fried. Even raw they were not so bad. They tasted very much like anchovies. My tame dolphins remained absolutely faithful, above all "Dora," who seemed larger than ever and never gave me the slightest opportunity of catching her.

That day the sun was very strong. The night was cool and extremely pleasant. I could still just hear the radio, providing I did not have it on for more than ten minutes at a time, sufficient on that day to learn that there had been a storm over Boulogne and Dunkirk. Poor Ginette, I thought, how worried she must be. I wanted the whole thing to end as quickly as possible more for her sake than for mine. My own chief preoccupation was to lose no more latitude.

Then the radio suddenly went silent for good. I was on Latitude 17° 14', which runs to the north of Guadeloupe, between Antigua and Barbuda. I noted:

"Am always in a hurry for night to fall, first of all because it means another day gone, secondly because I can go to sleep trusting in Providence, and finally because I see nothing to upset me."

This sort of passivity is typical of anyone who has been alone for a long time. He finishes by no longer dominating his surroundings but bowing his head to whatever happens next. Any day not marked by some disturbing event is a good day, and an uneventful night is infinitely reassuring.

That day I was followed in the water by a long, green sausage, about ten feet long and nine inches or so in diameter. It was not a seaweed because it moved and wriggled. It finally cured me of any ideas of a swim.

The next day, November 9, the fresh wind became even stronger. I was well pleased, as it pushed my speed up considerably, but I was worried about my patched sail. I got very wet during the night and was afraid I would pay dearly for my swifter progress by helpless immobility if my sail were carried away.

That day, including the one I left, was my fourth Sunday at sea. I hoped there were only two more. From Monday, I was going to be able to talk to myself about "next week."

I was tired of eating flying fish. Although they made splendid bait for the dolphins, I'd had enough. During the night of the ninth to tenth, and during most of the following day, the wind remained strong. I was going along at a fine clip, but haunted by the strain on the sail. For a whole week I had not seen another ship, but for the first time I caught a really big flying fish, about the size of a large mackerel. It was delicious.

"There are some big clouds gathering. It is going to be difficult to take my position tomorrow."

Suddenly I was threatened again by the ever-present danger of swamping. A wave broke near me and half filled the boat, momentarily threatening a capsize. By now I was convinced that if the worst happened, it would mean death. With this in mind, I had put a little packet of barbiturates in my shirt pocket. I had made up my mind that if I was flung into the water, I was not going to fight it out for thirty hours or more. There was not the slightest possibility of receiving any sort of help. I thought the best thing was to put myself to sleep right away.

Although it might be supposed that my senses had become deadened, my fears increased. I had been at sea for twenty days, always with the realization that one wave might finish me. The fact that the boat had at no time been in mortal danger made no difference. I was to remain at the mercy of that single wave until the last day of the voyage. I still thought it would only be another ten days before I reached the shipping routes. Until then there was certainly no hope of succor.

CHAPTER 12

Mid-Passage

LAND! LAND! is the cry of the castaway when he sights the first coast. My cry on November 11 was Rain! Rain!

I had noticed for some time that the surface of the sea had become strangely calm, exactly as if oil had been poured on it, when suddenly I shouted out: "Rain! Here comes the rain."

I undressed so that I would be ready to wash all the salt off my body and then sat down on one of the floats. I held between my legs an inflatable rubber mattress, capable of holding some fifteen gallons of water and stretched the tent over it. I waited. Like the sound of a soda siphon, monstrously magnified, I heard advancing from far away the noise of water beating on water. I must have waited nearly twenty minutes, watching the slow approach of this manna from heaven. The waves were flattened under the weight of the rain, and the wind buffeted me as the squall hit the boat. The cloud passed over slowly, writhing with the vertical turbulence of a small cyclone. I was drenched in a tropical downpour, which rapidly filled the tent sheet and made it sag with the weight between my knees. I plunged my head in it and as quickly spat the water out again. It was full of salt from the tent and I let it all spill overboard. At the second fill, although the water tasted of rubber, it was like nectar. I washed myself voluptuously. The squall did not last long, but the rainfall was tremendous. I not only drank my fill that day, but was also able to store three or four gallons in my rubber mattress. I was going to have a gurgling pillow, but each night my reserve of water would renew my hopes for the next day. Even if I had nothing to eat, even if I caught no fish, I at least had something to drink.

Even though I had not had a drop of fresh water for three weeks, just the liquid I pressed from my fish, my reactions were perfectly normal, including the marvelous sensation of at last swallowing a real drink. My skin was still in perfect order, although much affected by the salt; my mucous membranes had not dried; and my urine had remained normal in quantity, odor, and color. I had proved conclusively that a castaway could live for three weeks (and even longer, because I could have continued perfectly well) without fresh water. It is true, Providence was to spare me the ordeal of having to rely again on the flat, insipid fish juice. From that day on I always had sufficient rain water to slake my thirst. It sometimes seemed as if my stock were about to run out, but a shower always came in time.

I had tried in vain to wash the salt out of my clothes and bedding. Alas, I was to remain until the end "a man of salt water," as the Polynesians say, completely encrusted with it until the day of my arrival.

That day brought me both pleasure and perturbation. The pleasure consisted in a new sort of bird, an attractive creature called, in English, I believe, a "white-tailed tropic bird," and which the French call a *"paille-cul."* It looks like a white dove with a black beak, with a long plume in its tail. With an impertinent air, it uses this plume as an elevator. I rummaged quickly for my raft book, written for the use of castaways, and read that the appearance of this bird did not necessarily mean that one was near land. But as it could only come from the American Continent, being completely unknown in Europe, it was a good sign. For the first time, I had met a bird which came, without a shadow of doubt, from my destination.

This pleasant interlude was followed about two o'clock in the afternoon by a number of hours of terror, lasting until two the next morning. Just as I was peacefully reading a little Aeschylus, there was a violent blow on the rudder: "That's another shark," I thought, and looked up. What I saw was a large swordfish of undeniably menacing aspect. He was following the dinghy at a distance of about twenty feet, seemingly in a rage, his dorsal fin raised like hackles. In one of his feints around the boat, he had collided with my rudder oar. I found I had a determined enemy. If I succeeded only in wounding him, he would surely attack again, and that would be the end of *L'Hérétique*. What was worse, as I was hurriedly getting my harpoon ready, a clumsy movement dropped it into the sea. It was my last one. Now I was unarmed. I fixed my pocketknife onto my underwater gun as a makeshift bayonet, determined to sell my life dearly if he attacked in earnest.

This intolerable anguish lasted twelve long hours. As night fell, I could follow the swordfish's movements by his luminous wake and the noise his dorsal fin made cutting the water. Several times his back bumped the underside of the dinghy, but he still seemed a little afraid of me. He never approached from ahead, but every time he came at me he changed course at the last moment before striking the floats. I came to believe that he was frightened; probably as frightened as I was. In the early hours of the morning his wake disappeared, but I had spent a sleepless night.

One of the lulls in this encounter brought a minor relief, which I interpreted as a message from the land. It was one of those little glass floats used on fishing nets and encrusted with little shellfish, Cirripedia, and other sorts of barnacle. It had clearly been in the water a long time, but it was a sign of human life.

It was an exhausting day. By the time it was over I was utterly miserable. It even rained so hard during the night that I thought I was going to have too much fresh water after having gone without it for so long. I wrote:

"It would really be too much if I drowned in fresh water, but that is what is going to happen if this downpour goes on. I have enough for a month. My God, what a cloudburst! What is more, the sea is rising. A pale sun poked through this morning, but it is still raining."

I saw my first clump of seaweed, or at least so I thought. (In fact, it was a magnificent jellyfish, the float blue and violet, of the type known as a Portuguese man-of-war.) Its long treacherous filaments, hanging to a considerable depth, can cause dangerous stings, which often develop into ulcers.

I realized, after one or two wakeful nights, how essential it was to get a good sleep: "Forty-eight hours without sleep and I am utterly depressed; the ordeal is really beginning to get me down. Moreover, the sea is infested with tunny and swordfish. I can see them leaping all around me. I do not mind the tunny and the birds so much, but the swordfish are a real menace. Am making good speed, but would willingly add another five or six days to the voyage if I could rest up in comparative calm. This dark, forbidding sea has a depressing effect." It really seemed as if the sea were in mourning. It was as black as ink, flecked from time to time by a white crest, which the plankton made luminous by night. It looked like an evening dress with occasional white flowers, or a Japanese mourning robe. Not a star to be seen and the low sky seemed about to crush me. I realized the full meaning of the term "heavy weather"; it felt like a physical weight on my shoulders.

At five o'clock on November 12, I noted: "Rain and yet more rain; this is more than I can stand. But I wonder if I am not nearer the coast than I think, as there are several more birds. There are ten round me at the same time, and my bird book says that more than six mean that one is not more than a hundred or two hundred miles from the coast." Little did I think that I was only just over a hundred miles away from the Cape Verde Islands.

During the night of November twelfth to thirteenth, I had another visit from a shark, or at least I assumed it was a shark. How was I to know whether it was a shark or a swordfish? Every time a shark appeared during the day, I felt perfectly safe. I gave it the ritual clout on the nose and off it went. But during the night, fearing that one of those devilish creatures might spear me with his sword, I was no longer able to be so bold. I had to remain watchfully awake, trying to identify the intruder, and waiting wide-eyed for it to make off. Sleep was effectively banished. And often it seemed that the sharks or some other animals played some sort of ball game during the night with my dinghy. I didn't dare to interfere.

It was still raining in torrents. Under such a deluge I was obliged to stretch the tent right over my head, but it formed great pockets of water which trickled down through the gaps. After a certain time, the weight threatened to break the guy ropes, and I had to push from underneath to spill the water overboard. It must be difficult to realize the sacrifice involved for a castaway in thus jettisoning his reserve of fresh water. Even without sharks and swordfish, sleep had become practically impossible. The rain thundered down, and every quarter of an hour or so I had to heave it overboard. An unbelievable quantity of water fell on the tent and trickled through every crevice.

I began to believe, in a confused sort of way, in the active hostility of certain inanimate objects. I might decide to write up my log or work out some calculation. I would sit down with a pencil. I needed only to turn around for ten seconds, and the pencil would disappear. It was like a mild form of persecution mania, although up till then I had always been able to meet such annoyances with good humor, by thinking of the similar misfortunes suffered by the Three Men in a Boat.

"*Friday, November 14.* The last forty-eight hours have been the worst of the voyage. I am covered with little spots, and my tongue is coated. I do not like the look of things at all. The storm has been short and violent. Was obliged to launch the sea anchor for several hours, but hoisted sail again at nine-thirty. Still raining in sheets, and everything soaked through. Morale still fairly good, but I am starting to get physically tired of the perpetual wetness, which there is no sun to dry. I do not think I have lost a great deal of time, but it is impossible to determine my latitude as can see neither sun nor stars, and another of these confounded rainstorms is blowing up from the horizon. The sea is calmer, but yesterday I shipped plenty. They do say: 'Fine weather follows rain.' I can hardly wait for it."

During the night a tremendous wave, catching me by the stern, carried me along at great speed and then flooded *L'Hérétique,* breaking my rudder oar at the same time. The dinghy immediately turned broadside on, and my sail started to flap in a sinister manner, straining at my rough stitches. I plunged forward to gather it in but stumbled against the tent and tore a great rent near the top of one of the poles. There would be no way of mending it properly, and it happened just as I had to battle for life with the waves. I threw out both my sea anchors. Docilely, *L'Hérétique* turned its stern to my normal course and faced up to its assailants. By this time, I was at the end of my strength and, in the face of all the risks, I decided that sleep was the first necessity. I closed up the tent as hermetically as I could and made up my mind to sleep for twenty-four hours, whatever the weather did and whatever happened.

The squalls continued for another ten hours, during which my eggshell craft behaved admirably. But the danger was not yet passed. The worst moments came after the wind had dropped and the sea continued to rage. The wind seemed to enforce a sort of discipline on the sea, propelling the waves without giving them time to break. Left to itself, the sea took much longer to calm its anger. It broke with all its force in every direction, shattering everything in its path.

"*Saturday, November 15, 1330.* Taking advantage of the rain to do a little writing. Have only two rudder oars left. Hope they will hold out. Rain has been coming down in torrents since ten o'clock yesterday evening. No sign of the sun; am wet through. Everything is soaked and I have no means of drying a thing; my sleeping bag looks like a wet sack. No hope of taking my position. The weather was so bad during the night that I wondered for a time if I had not drifted into the Doldrums. Fortunately, there is no doubt that the trade wind is still with me. Making good time; almost too fast for comfort. Still worried about the sail. When will the weather clear up? There was one patch of blue sky in the west, but the wind is from the east. Perhaps tomorrow will be better, but I am going to have another thick night. About seven o'clock this morning an aircraft flew over me quite low. Tried to signal it, but my torch would not work. First sign of human life since November 3; hope there will be more. Sky to the west now clearing rapidly; difficult to understand why."

There was a sort of battle in the sky that whole day between the two fronts of good and bad weather. I called it the fight between the blue and the black. It started with the appearance in the west of a little patch of blue, no bigger than a gendarme's cap, as the French song has it, and there seemed little hope of its growing. The black clouds, impenetrable as ink, seemed fully conscious of their power and marched in serried ranks to attack the tiny blue intruder; but the blue patch seemed to call up reinforcements on its wings, and in a few hours, to the south and north, that is to say, to my left and right, several more blue patches had appeared, all seemingly about to be engulfed in the great black flood advancing toward them. But where the clouds concentrated on frontal attacks, the blue of the sky used infiltration tactics, breaking up the mass of black until the good weather predominated. By four o'clock in the afternoon its victory was clear. My log entry for that day read: "Thank God for the sun! I am covered with little spots, but the sun is back." Little did I know that the most harrowing part of my voyage was about to begin.

I had not the faintest idea where I was. With no sun for three days I was in a state of complete ignorance. On Sunday, the sixteenth, when I got my sextant ready, I was in a fever of apprehension. By a miracle, I had not drifted much to the south. I was still on Latitude 16° 59', which passes to the north of Guadeloupe. That vital point was settled, but my boat looked like a battlefield. My hat had blown off in the storm, and all I now had as protection for my head was a little white bonnet, which I had made out of a piece of waterproofed linen, quite inadequate in such a climate. The tent was torn in two places. Although the dinghy seemed to have suffered no damage, everything in it was drenched. Even after the long sunny days which were to come, the night dew continued to reimpregnate my warm clothes and sleeping bag, so I was never again to know a dry night until I touched land.

A disturbing incident then showed that I could not afford to relax my vigilance for one moment. During the storm, I had tried to protect the afterpart of L'Hérétique from the breaking waves by trailing a large piece of rubberized cloth fixed firmly to the ends of my two floats. This seemed to divert the force of the waves as they broke behind me. Even though the storm had died down, I saw no point in removing this protection. But the following night, a frightful noise brought me out of my sleeping bag at one bound. My protective tail was no longer there. It had been torn away. I checked anxiously to make sure that the floats had not been damaged and that they were still firmly inflated. Some unseen creature, probably attracted by the vivid yellow color of the cloth which hung down between the floats, had torn it off by jumping out of the water. This it had done with such precision that there was no other visible sign of its attack.

Like the boat, I had also taken a buffeting. I was much weakened, and every movement made me terribly tired, rather like the period after my long fast in the Mediterranean. I was much thinner and was particularly worried about the state of my skin. My whole body was covered with tiny red spots. At first they were little more than surface discolorations, not perceptible to the touch, but in a day or two they became little hard lumps that finally developed into pustules. I was mortally afraid of a bad attack of boils, which, in the condition I was in, would have had serious consequences. The pain alone would have proved unbearable, and I would no longer have been able to sit or lie down.

The only medication I had on board for treating infections was Mercurochrome and penicillin. During the night, the pain became so bad that I could not bear to have anything in contact with my skin. On top of this, the least little abrasion seemed to turn septic, so I had to disinfect them all very carefully. Between the two, I was so spotted with Mercurochrome that I looked as if I were covered with blood. The skin under my nails was all inflamed, and little pockets of pus, very painful, formed under half of them. I had to lance them without an anesthetic. I could have used some of the penicillin but I wanted to keep up my medical observations with a minimum of treatment for as long as I could stand it. My feet were peeling in great strips and within three days I lost the nails from four toes.

I never would have been able to hold out if the deck had not been made of wood, which I regard as an essential piece of equipment in a life raft: essential because it prevents the skin from becoming softened by constant contact with sea water. Without a wooden deck I would have developed gangrene or, at the very least, serious arterial trouble.

For the time being, however, my ailments were still localized. My blood pressure remained good and I was still perspiring normally. In spite of that, I greeted with relief the victorious sun which appeared on the sixteenth, expecting it to cure the effects of the constant humidity which I had endured. I did not know that the sun was to cause even worse ordeals during the cruel twenty-seven days which were to follow.

The castaway must never give way to despair. Even when things seem at their worst, something will happen to effect a transformation. But it is equally unwise to become too hopeful; it would never do to forget that however unbearable an ordeal may seem, there may be another to come which effaces the memory of the first. If a toothache becomes intolerable, it might almost seem a relief to exchange it for an earache. But with a really bad pain in the ear, the memory of the toothache becomes a distinctly lesser evil. The best advice that I can give is that whether things go well or ill, the castaway must try to maintain a measure of detachment. The days of rain had been bad enough, but what followed, in spite of the rosy future the sun at first seemed to promise, was to seem much worse.

November 16 was my twenty-ninth day at sea, and I had every reason for optimism. There had been a decline in my health, but at least the worst part of the journey was now behind me. Up till then I had had to maintain a course across the wind, but now I was sailing directly before it. I had collected enough fresh water for about a month, and the fish which had accompanied me from the start still surrounded the boat. The old hands, those that I had succeeded in wounding during the first few days, had not forgotten their experience and still remained out of reach. Every morning I saw them rise from the depths, give me a suspicious look, and then take up their position on a parallel course. Their company became increasingly welcome, first because they were old friends, and chiefly because they encouraged other fish to join them. The newcomers arrived in shoals, duped by their more cunning relations, and sported all around me, providing an endless supply of innocent victims.

Certain "specialists" had advised me to install a small tank in the bottom of the boat in which to keep the fish I caught. The reader will by now appreciate how superfluous such advice was.

My larder followed me wherever I went. Not only that, but my faithful companions chased unlimited flying fish in my direction. Scared into flight by the dolphins, they continually crashed into my sail, and I picked up five or ten every morning. This never happened during the day, presumably because they saw me and could avoid the obstacle. There was never an interval of more than five minutes before a squadron or two took to the air. The ingenuity and skill with which the dolphins chased them, after flushing a covey, was a spectacle of which I never tired. With wide-open mouths, they usually managed to be at the exact spot where the flying fish hit the water again. A few of the intended victims, probably taught by experience, changed direction in mid-air and, by bouncing from wave crest to wave crest, managed to elude their pursuers.

Once the storm was over, I carried out an underwater inspection of the dinghy, with a secure life line around my waist. Almost all the repairs effected at Las Palmas had succumbed to the battering of the sea. The glue had not held, and strips of rubberized fabric fluttered down lamentably. A whole colony of Cirripedia, a type of barnacle, had attached themselves along the seams. Of all the experts familiar with my type of boat, only M. Debroutelle, the manufacturer of the dinghy, and a real specialist in everything that concerned it, had warned me: "You cannot expect to avoid barnacles."

The one detail of the *L'Hérétique's* construction which I considered a potential weakness was the seams which connected the sections of fabric. There was little likelihood of the floats bursting from internal pressure. Every seam had been covered with a safety band, but it was still possible for these tiny shellfish to penetrate underneath it, tearing it loose as they grew. I had already noticed at Tangier that even when the dinghy was moored in a deep bay, a dense submarine growth attached itself to the bottom, particularly along the seams. The main seams held the stern board in position between the rubber bottom and the floats and secured the floats to the rubber bottom.

From Casablanca to the Canaries, the depth of the water and the speed at which I traveled arrested the growth of these marine parasites, but during the time I spent at Las Palmas, the bottom of the dinghy became covered with an absolute forest of seaweed and barnacles. After I had scraped it off, I noticed with foreboding the little bumps under my safety bands where some of the organisms had penetrated, and I therefore stuck on a double layer. These were precisely the points where the fabric had given way. I could carry out no further repairs under water and had no choice but to trust in the confidence which M. Debroutelle had in his boat, and climbed back aboard without much difficulty.

CHAPTER 13

Longitude

"SUNDAY, NOVEMBER 16. It is now four weeks since I left. Have been able to take my latitude for the first time in four days. In spite of everything, have remained on the seventeenth parallel (16° 59′, to be exact). This is perfect: I shall land somewhere between Guadeloupe, Monserrat, and Antigua. With any luck, I should arrive between Saturday, the twenty-second, and Saturday, November 29, the two extreme limits of time. Something bumped me again during the night; I do not know what it was, but the pieces of fabric I had fixed again to prevent waves breaking into the boat have been torn away. There must be some unpleasant company around. Hot sun, but plenty of spray.

"*Four o'clock.* Another swordfish, confound it! But this one is quite small. He made one quick turn around me and then made off, but I still do not like it.

"*Monday, November 17.* Wind light during the night, but sea very rough. This morning I understand why: a fine storm is blowing up. The whole eastern sky looks threatening. Plenty of birds.

"*Four o'clock.* Managed to take my approximate position all right, but it is by no means easy in such a heavy sea. Wind has picked up and I am making good speed. The next few days are not going to be easy and I am by no means confident that I have calculated my position correctly. If only I could meet a boat so that I could confirm it! Theoretically, I have only about five hundred miles to go. It would be unbearable to fail now. Sometimes I want the week to end and at others I do not. Sky looks threatening, but good speed is the main thing. Should sight land in six days if all is well. Feel tired and would like, above all: (1) a hot bath; (2) watertight shoes; (3) a dry bed; (4) a roast chicken; (5) a quart of beer.

"Still plenty of flying fish; not daring to put out lines, for I might catch a swordfish and make him lose his temper. Am also putting off the moment for showing a light at night; the danger of a swordfish attack seems greater than that of being run down. Do not like look of the sea. Feel afraid of it; more so than at the start. Curiously, the sea is not at its most dangerous when the waves are high; only when it is not controlled by the wind. It is dangerous when a storm is gathering, because it is not yet under control; also when it has blown itself out and no longer gives the sea a rhythm. I am going to pass a bad night, I can see that.

"*Tuesday, November 18.* Morale higher today, but time is beginning to weigh. Start to think about the problem of landing. If I keep on this latitude I shall end up either at Port Louis or Pointe-à-Pitre in Guadeloupe. All the harbors are protected from the wind and difficult for me to enter, but if I miss Pointe-à-Pitre I shall be in the Caribbean Sea. If I am north of Latitude 16° 30', I shall try for the north coast, either Désirade or Marie-Galante. Cannot bear the idea of having some accident while landing and prefer not to think about it. Sufficient unto the day . . . ! Decide to send off a message in a bottle; it will be amusing to see if it is picked up.

"*Wednesday, November 19.* Had a shock when I took my latitude; I had been carried twenty miles to the south compared with yesterday. Found after a check that I had misread the sextant. Thank goodness for that. After the midday sight, the long afternoon hours. Am fishing again and catch all I need in the morning, so there is nothing left to do but ruminate on the possible day of my arrival. Getting very bored. Sun scorching, but weather uncertain. Continue to do my daily physical checkup and still have something to read. More rain this morning.

"*Thursday, November 20.* Steering due west on Latitude 16° 48′, which should bring me between Guadeloupe and Antigua. If I can maintain this, will try and land on Guadeloupe, which is French territory. Spent one of the best nights of the voyage; plenty of birds. One thing makes me feel I must be getting near land: the wind blows from eight o'clock to eleven-thirty, when it drops, freshening again at three o'clock. This, I remember, is the pattern near the coast. Must concentrate entirely on keeping this course. Probably have another week to go, but at least until then promise myself not to despair. Poor Ginette must be worried to death. For her sake I would like to get there as soon as possible.

"*Friday, November 21.* The nearer I think I am, the more doubts I have about my exact position, but it ought to be correct. Still no sign of a ship, but I must remember that on the way to the Canaries I only saw two, and those quite close to land. Take heart from the birds, which I see flying off to the east in the morning and flying back toward the west in the evening, presumably on their day's flight from the land. This seems a good sign. Weather variable, but quite good; wind uneven. Am in a real hurry to get there. Have decided to show a light at night. It brings me an absolute shower of flying fish. Must arrive between Saturday, the twenty-second, and Saturday, the twenty-ninth. Monday, Tuesday, or Wednesday are the most likely days. Still on Latitude 16° 48′. Good!

"*Saturday, November 22.* Very little wind. I am crawling like a tortoise. At this speed it will take at least another week. As I feared, these days are proving a great strain. In spite of myself I do nothing but scan the horizon. Every cloud looks like the first shadow of land, although I know I cannot possibly see any until Monday. So avid for the sight of it that I am prepared to remain on watch for a week. Large increase in the number of land birds, that must mean something. Still no sign of a ship. Wind has picked up, praise God.

"*1300 hours.* Heat tropical; how poor Ginette must be suffering, morally and physically. 'My dear, in another four or five days your worries will be over.' If only the trade wind would freshen!

"*1730 hours.* If the wind remains like this, it will take me ten days to sight land.

"*Sunday, November 23.* Sixth Sunday at sea; can only hope it is the last. The wind has picked up and seems steady; if it keeps that way, I shall arrive Tuesday or Wednesday, but cannot tell where, as I am drifting somewhat to the northward. Have sighted a couple of curious creatures that look like trigger fish, but their two fins resemble those of a shark. Tried to catch one of them, but without success. Pity; am getting a little tired of flying fish.

"*1700 hours.* A small storm is brewing to the southwest. No half measures about this weather; either a burning sun without a cloud in sight or a thunderstorm. The wretched fish, nibbling at my barnacles, keep butting the bottom of the boat, a most disagreeable feeling. The storm is now gathering. I hope it does not hit me too hard. Not too worried, however fierce it is, as I cannot be far from my destination now. Saw three white-tailed tropic birds together this morning, and my castaway's handbook says that this means that land cannot be more than eighty miles away. Just as the storm reached me, a frigate bird flew over. Another encouraging note in the handbook: 'The frigate bird never spends the night at sea and is seldom found more than a hundred miles from land. In one exceptional instance, one was sighted three hundred miles from the nearest coast.' At two o'clock in the afternoon I saw a northern gannet not very far away, another bird seldom seen more than ninety miles out to sea. All this confirms that I cannot have far to go."

Before the storm clouds started to gather on the horizon, I had begun to feel curiously uneasy. Perhaps that is not the right word, but I felt a strong compulsion to flee, to get away from where I was. I could not tell why, but I would have liked to find myself somewhere else, and quickly at that. There was little to distinguish my situation from that of the creatures in the sea around me. I must have acquired some part of their instincts. I took out my *Pilot Book* to read the section dealing with indications of a typhoon. I scrutinized every point of the compass and saw only gold flecks in the sky and a few black patches gathering on the horizon, nothing alarming, but I still felt that something unpleasant was going to happen. I felt quite unable to escape what I was sure was some impending catastrophe making straight for me. Some time after I arrived in Barbados I discovered that in a number of ships a hundred miles or so to the north, the crews had experienced the same feeling of disquiet. There appears to be a subtle but powerful communion of thought processes among those who ply the sea.

Right across the horizon behind me, barely visible, appeared a line of black, as if drawn with a ruler, which seemed to prevent the sun from rising. There was a slow drop in the temperature, and the black line spread across the sky like an awning. Starting at six o'clock in the morning, it did not complete its slow progress until seven o'clock in the evening, but it did not seem to be preceded by any freshening of the wind. The sea remained calm and I thought I would be able to keep my sail hoisted and still weather the approaching storm. Then I heard a characteristic noise I knew so well, like a forest fire or a machine gun; rain was pouring down from the black mass, sounding like thousands of fir cones thrown into a fire. Then the storm was upon me, with a sudden buffet of wind which somehow did not seem part of it but was no less violent for that. I made up my mind to take advantage of it for as long as possible, holding the mainsheet of my sail in my hand, ready to let it go if the pressure proved too great. Day was turned into night, and with the raindrops hitting the sea like sparks, my sail suddenly filled like a balloon. The storm did not rage for long, but was terrifying while it lasted. For an hour, wrapping the mainsheet around my wrist, I tore through the fury of the elements at five knots or more. When it was over, my hand was covered with blood from the friction of the rope. With no transition period, the moment the rear edge of the storm cloud passed over me, the wind disappeared completely, and for the first time since I had left the Canaries the sail started to flap, and then drooped, inert. I was convinced that the worst was now over and the long period of bad weather, strong winds, and excessive spray at an end. I was to experience yet another evil that used to beset sailing ships: a prolonged dead calm. I think the notes I made in my logbook at the time express better than any subsequent commentary the anguish into which this exasperating state of affairs was to plunge me.

"*Monday, November 24.* I was right: one should not count one's chickens before they are hatched. After the storm, the only faint breeze is coming from due south. With the drift, I am having serious trouble in maintaining a compass route of 320°, which is carrying me dangerously to the north. I am terribly afraid of getting caught in the Gulf Stream and carried northward. [It must not be forgotten that I still thought I had arrived roughly at the junction of the northern Equatorial Current and the Gulf Stream.] This would mean another month. Feeling very disheartened. If I get carried up to Latitude 23° or 24°, I shall be frozen, as it is now winter there. If only I could meet a ship! The wind must change. And to think I had only ninety miles to go! This could only happen to me. The trade wind seems to have completely disappeared. Am terribly afraid there will be days and days of this, and I was so near.

"*1500 hours.* Weather conditions still the same but am feeling a little better. I see in the *Pilot Book* that these disturbances are only temporary and the trade wind soon re-establishes itself. Nevertheless, have lost a lot of time. Guadeloupe is now at least a hundred miles away, and I may now have to make either for Barbuda, 17° 40′ North, 61° 50′ West, a hundred and twenty miles away; Barbados, 13° 10′ North, 50° 30′ West; or even Puerto Rico, four hundred miles away. That is to say, either another week, providing the wind returns, or anything up to six months. Am, in fact, nineteen minutes of latitude farther north, on the parallel which passes between Barbuda and Antigua. If only the weather would change. What filthy luck just as I was nearly there. If only I could sight a ship! But there is nothing, absolutely nothing in sight.

"*Tuesday, November 25.* The wind has veered a little and is now blowing from ESE. Have been able to regain about eleven miles to the south and am now on Latitude 17° 05′, on a better course. That is not too bad, but fear the next few days may be very difficult and depressing after all this delay. If my calculations of longitude are right, I am only sixty miles from the nearest land, but cannot be sure. Must see land tomorrow, otherwise I shall have no idea where I am. My course is all right, but I shall have no idea how far I have progressed along it. Taking the most pessimistic estimate, I could be about seven degrees farther east, about four hundred and six miles away, or six days' sailing at this speed. Must not lose heart before Tuesday, December 2. If nothing has happened by then, I shall be completely baffled. How long the days are! Even my four o'clock petrel has disappeared; he paid me a visit the day before yesterday, but I did not see him yesterday for the first time during the voyage. I wonder if he flew back to land or farther out to sea. For all I see of them, every ship in the world might have sunk and every airplane crashed.

"*Wednesday, November 26.* Saw two more frigate birds this morning, so land should be less than a hundred miles away if what is said about them is true. Perhaps I am right about my position after all. Visibility poor, as it was near the Canaries, only about fifteen miles, and these islands are thirty miles apart. Hope there will be no repetition of what nearly happened in the

Canaries, when I almost passed between them without seeing either. If I know I have passed them, I will steer northwest for Puerto Rico. If there is no means of telling, then anything may happen. And to think that the day before yesterday visibility must have been at least forty miles. Confound that storm! Am still trying to get back to the latitude of Guadeloupe and stay between 16° and 16° 30′ North.

"*1500 hours.* Crawling like a tortoise. I cannot be more than sixty miles from Antigua and am hardly moving. If I am making thirty miles a day, it would be a miracle. These last two hundred miles could have been measured by the yard, but this cannot last more than forty-eight or seventy-two hours (!). Now that I really seem near, time is passing more slowly than ever. Am incapable of realizing that it is possible, even probable, that by this time on Tuesday I shall be on terra firma. I just cannot picture it.

"*Thursday, November 27.* This slowness is exasperating. I would be lucky to have made twenty miles since Sunday. It is beginning to look more like next Tuesday or Wednesday; another ten days of torture. I have really had enough, and with this visibility am in constant fear of missing the islands. It is a terrible strain to keep scanning the horizon. My eyes are focusing on it all the time, and I have no dark glasses to reduce the glare of the sun. No ships, no planes, no birds. *I have had enough* [underlined in my log]; forty days is enough for any man.

"*1800 hours.* Caught a fly in the boat; this must be a good sign. Land cannot be far away.

"*Friday, November 28, 9 o'clock.* Still nothing in sight this morning; am really getting perturbed. Poor Ginette; forty-one days and no news of me. But my sight at moonset confirmed that land can be only sixty miles away. I am on the right latitude, but hardly making any headway. Passed a lamp bulb floating in the water, of all curious things. Am absolutely browned off.

"*1900 hours.* Quite a nice fresh little breeze, better than anything in a week. If it keeps up, I should sight land within eighteen hours. No sign of a ship since Monday, November 3.

"*Saturday, November 29.* That breeze lasted exactly ten minutes; sky leaden; temperature a hundred degrees under my tent; no wind, no land, no ship, no plane, no birds; desperate.

"Am hardly making way, probably half a mile an hour. This is going to take another ten or twenty days, although I was told that the trade wind blew right across. Alarmed at the thought of how anxious my family must be. If only I could meet a boat which would pass on news of me, but there is absolutely nothing to be seen. Caught a trigger fish today with my knife on the end of an oar; hesitate to eat it, as one book calls it edible and another poisonous. Prefer to take no risk. You would think that those who have studied the problems of castaways would agree about something.

"*1900 hours.* Wind springs up just as it did yesterday. If only it would last. Launched another message in a bottle. Boat followed by a large barracuda, a new sort of fish, so land must be near. Try to catch him, but he avoids me with a dirty look. Think he would probably like to eat me.

"*Sunday, November 30.* A whole week of near immobility. Confound the wretches who said the trade wind would blow all the way. Eight days of calm; nothing in sight. Have a bad attack of diarrhea, which obliges me to squat over the side twenty times a day. The trade wind is a snare and a delusion; it takes you three-quarters of the way across and then abandons you. And this is supposed to be the best time of year for it. Must resign myself. Supposing I had made thirty miles a day; that would give me an average of fifty-five miles a day since the start. This means arriving on Sunday, December 7, another week. Patience. But then I give up.

"*Monday, December 1.* So there I am, November over and still no sight of land. Prey to every emotion. The hour of moonrise would seem to put me on 50° of longitude and its setting on 60°. Am absolutely stymied. Full moon tonight; we shall see. Making some headway with a light breeze which has sprung up, but it was flat calm during the whole night. Am I forty or twelve hundred miles away? Real torrid heat; horizon empty and hazy. If only I knew my longitude for certain, had a battery for the radio set and a proper chronometer. Had a morning visit from a white-tail, which nearly alighted on a float. Took a snap of him, but when I got out my movie camera, he took fright and flew off into the sun.

"*1100 hours*. Knowing her as I do, am really worried about Ginette; she must be thin and miserable, and there may be another ten days of this. Worn out and anxious myself. This diarrhea is starting to get me down. Signs of blood in the stool; hope it is nothing serious.

"*1500 hours*. Latitude still perfect; something of a breeze, and a frigate bird, the fourth in five days, has arrived to cheer me up. As three hundred miles out is apparently their maximum, and I have been seeing them for five days, I cannot have much more than a hundred miles to go. Hope springs eternal.

"*1800 hours*. Have just looked through my pictures of France, Casablanca, and Las Palmas. It was a mistake. Now I am really depressed. The ordeal has gone on too long and this uncertainty as to my position is the last straw. I must be right within two hundred miles or so, but shall I arrive the day after tomorrow or in ten, twenty, or thirty days? I have no idea and am beginning to wish I had stopped in the Canaries. Then my pride reproaches me. If only I could sight a ship. If I could hear the radio, I would feel less alone. As for the fellow who assured me that the wind would blow from the northeast right till the end, I'll get even with him yet. Since the storm, there has been either no wind at all or it has come from the southeast.

"*Tuesday, December 2*. [My morale was very low, and the log is quite difficult to decipher.] Still nothing in sight; saw a new type of bird this morning, a Manx shearwater, also described as not flying more than a hundred miles out to sea.

"This seems to be the evidence for and against the proximity of land:

"Against: Hour of sunrise, sunset, zenith, and moonrise. But the first three already showed an error of about an hour on my departure, when I knew my longitude. The hour of moonrise would put me at about 50° West, but this is contradicted by the reading given when it sets.

"For: Hour of moonset, which makes me about 60° West, irregularity of the wind which falls at night, frigate bird, few birds in general but new types and not a single albatross. I have made fifty or sixty miles a day, which was my average on the first lap to the Canaries, that is to say, between two thousand and twenty-four hundred miles; there can be only between a hundred and eighty and three hundred and eighty miles to go.

"At best I am at Longitude 59° or 60°, at worst only at 50°.

"If the wind had held, I would have been ashore a week ago, but it is extremely light and only blows five or six hours a day, less than between Tangier and Casablanca. It looks as if I shall never cover the remaining two or three hundred miles. Nothing is more exasperating than to have logged twenty-five hundred in a month and then need thirty days for the remaining three hundred. Still no sign of a wind; it is really too much. Am beginning to lose hope completely. My experiment has now lasted forty-four days. I cannot bear the idea of failure so near success. If only I could pass on some news, but have seen neither plane nor boat. As for the raft book, all its information about birds is tripe and serves only to lower one's morale.

"*1500 hours.* What I fail to understand is this: my chief problem should have been to avoid drifting too far south, but for ten days that is where what wind there is has come from. What has happened to the northeast trade wind? Now forty-five days out, a month and a half, and Ginette still completely without news. Another day lost. Fortunately, few of them have been as cloudless as this, otherwise my skull would soon be at boiling point. Looks like another storm blowing up.

"*Wednesday, December 3*. [In spite of the trying circumstances in which they were written, I am continuing to give the entries in my log exactly as they appear.] Absolutely disgusted. The wind has swung around to the northeast again, after first veering west; a charming touch, but it is pretty feeble.

"*1100 hours*. Wind suddenly freshens for the first time in a week. If only it lasts.

"*1500 hours*. Stock of fresh water getting low. Need rain, but not too much!

"*1800 hours*. Another frigate bird; have given up counting how many I have seen. The raft book says they do not venture beyond a hundred miles. I hope that this time it is correct. If it had been right about the others, I would be there already. Diarrhea now very bad, and it seems to make me terribly thirsty. Would love to drink a quart of milk, just like that, at one gulp.

"*Thursday, December 4*. Nothing in sight, not a thing. Am beginning to feel physically exhausted. Visited today by a butterfly. Also saw a gossamer thread floating in the air, such as spiders spin on land. Surely after that, land cannot be far away. Score for ships and planes: nil.

"*Friday, December 5*. For all I know, the land is only a few dozen miles away, but that doesn't help me, as I still have no wind. Am worn out with this continuing diarrhea and hemorrhage. I hardly dare to eat any more; if this goes on, the boat may arrive but they will find me in it dead. Sky still leaden, not a cloud to be seen. Am completely baffled; have no idea where I am. If the dinghy is thrown up with me as a corpse, I only have one request and that is that someone goes and boxes the ears of the author of this *Castaways' Handbook*. It only serves to demoralize anyone who has been unfortunate enough to buy it. It states in black and white: 'A considerable number of frigate birds means that land is about a hundred miles away.' I have seen quite a number during the last week and have covered about three hundred miles. The only moral is that the author is dishonest to make statements he knows to be false, or if he has not confirmed them, then he should leave them out. The same applies to those who make assertions about the trade wind. It is perfectly clear that they have never had to make the journey themselves, or else they were in a ship with an engine. In the area of the West Indies, in November and December, there are two days of wind for every ten days of flat calm.

"Problem for the day: assuming that I am making a hundred yards an hour, how long will it take me to cover the hundred miles to land, if such a place exists. I shall be dead first, either burned to a crisp, or a victim of thirst and hunger. Everything seems to conspire against me. Since this morning I have literally been stewing in my own juice under a terrible sun. No shade, and yet barely half a mile away the sky is covered with thick clouds. It is frightening to realize to what extent one can develop a persecution mania alone on the surface of the sea; it really seems as if one is the victim of a conspiracy which one will never defeat. The wind is propelling several small cloud formations, but it seems as if they are deliberately avoiding the sun rather than pass across it and afford me a little shade.

"I am exhausted. If I fail, it will be because everything has turned against me; no wind and a scorching sun. Yesterday it rained all around the horizon, but not a drop fell into the boat. It is really too much. My sail is flapping from left to right. The trade wind, I presume. Definition of the trade wind area: a region where there is practically never any wind. I cannot even ascertain with certainty whether I am in the Doldrums. At this time of year they lie about Latitude 5° North, and in that case I would already have sighted land. This diarrhea is unbearable. One thing I know, the next time there is a storm, I will trust in

God, and under no circumstances put out the sea anchor. What have I done to deserve all this? After all, I could perfectly well have stopped in the Canaries.

"Jean-Luc, if I am dead on arrival, please publish a book made up of these entries as a small recompense to my wife. When people said that this crossing was possible, I should have taken it as an ill omen. Mediterranean, Casablanca, the Canaries were easy, although they were described as impossible. And now I am going to fail lamentably. How pleased a lot of people are going to be. I cannot stand the noise of this flapping sail. . . . This is the worst day of them all. I would prefer a good storm. Have thrown in the water some fluorescent stuff which makes a stain in the sea, in order to see how long I can keep it in sight. I may be making better time than I think. What really worries me is that up till now, even when I had very little wind, the clouds always indicated there was some at high altitudes. Today I do not even have that consolation. I hope this does not go on for another week. It is now thirty-two days since I saw a ship, and twenty-one since I sighted a plane; am utterly despondent. To think that Jack said: 'We shall never make it because of the wind, storms, and hurricanes'; but it is this flat calm which has caused disaster. If only I could send an SOS; even that would be a gamble. Not a single cloud passes across the sun, although there are plenty of them. I do not understand what is going on; lots of little flecks of low cloud are racing across the sky, but I am still in a dead calm such as I have seldom seen, not even in the Mediterranean. If only I could have a bath.

"*Saturday, December 6*. Quite a fresh breeze from the north; it is better than nothing. I saw three more white-tails together this morning; I can only suppose that land is sixty or eighty miles away. I cannot believe that the author of the *Castaways' Handbook* is wrong every time; perhaps, after all, I shall see land tomorrow or the day after. Come what may, I would like to record my last wishes, in case I am dead when the boat arrives:

"(1) I desire these notes to be made into a book, the rights to be held by Ginette Bombard, my wife. The following may be consulted on the background and reasons for this voyage: [then I listed several names].

"(2) [Here I gave certain instructions concerning provision for my wife and daughter.]

"(3) Steps must be taken to prevent the death of other castaways whose morale has been shattered by the authors of handbooks giving false information about signs of the proximity of land. Moreover, I hold responsible for my death those who prevented me from having the radio transmitter I so badly need at the moment.

"My thesis holds good for a duration of fifty days. If I am dead on arrival, there is no need for other castaways to despair. After that period, the strain on the human system is too great. It is highly desirable that astronomy courses in schools should include instruction in the principles of practical navigation.

"*Sunday, December 7*. Still nothing in sight, but I cannot be far away now. [At this point my writing became stronger and more legible.] I must get there alive, if only for Ginette and the children, but this suspense is terrible.

"The sun is implacable, and I am very thirsty. My supply of fresh water is running low. There cannot be more than about a gallon left; and to think how much I have thrown overboard! Barrels and barrels of it! Am doing very little fishing, but catching enough. With this horrible diarrhea, cannot bear the thought of having to start drinking sea water and fish juice again, am really feeling quite ill. Yesterday's north wind drove me eighteen miles to the south, carrying me away from La Désirade, the nearest land. Now it has dropped again; it is almost too much to bear. And there it stands in the *Pilot Book* [West Indies, Volume 2, lines 9–14]: "the trade wind is at its strongest and most regular from December to March or April. It is at that time at its farthest north and blows from ENE to NE, strength about 4 on the Beaufort scale." It is astonishing how many errors get into print! If I do not sight land tomorrow or the day after at the very latest, nothing will make sense and I shall give up. When I left, on about Longitude 15° 20′, I took my sight at about 1210 hours; today I took it at 1510 hours, a difference of three hours, which must place me at 60° 20′ West, La Désirade is on 61°, that is to say, thirty-eight miles farther west. Dominica and Marie-Galante are respectively 61° 20′ and 61° 12′ West, that is to say, fifty-six miles and forty-nine miles. Even at thirty miles a day, that cannot be more than two days' sailing. If I see nothing the day after tomorrow, I shall resign. I have had enough. All I can think of is poor Ginette, who must be dying a thousand deaths.

"*1630 hours.* Everything is stacked up against me; the wind has freshened but is driving me to the south. My luck is gone. However, everything is not lost. Even to the south, I have a certain amount of margin, as far as Grenada, two hundred and forty miles away; but this drift is going to mean further delay.

"Everything points to land being near, except for an actual sight of it; I keep passing pieces of floating wood, and for a while I was followed by what looked like a shoal of mullet, neither of which is a normal sight on the high seas. But all I want to see is some sort of coast line!

"*Monday, December 8.* Still nothing in sight and the wind has fallen again. I can hardly believe that people like the author of this *Castaways' Handbook* could be asked to write something for the official use of the American navy and fill it with nothing but misstatements. It says that a frigate bird has never been seen more than three hundred miles from the coast. Only admitting the evidence of the last one I saw, five days ago, there cannot have been more than three hundred miles to go even then.

"Saturday morning I again saw three tropic birds together. That is even more precise evidence: three of them mean that land is sixty or eighty miles away, say a hundred miles to be fair, and if I made forty miles from Saturday to Sunday and another forty since, there can only be another twenty to go. Still nothing in sight and another broiling day in prospect. I have been at sea fifty days, which would mean that I have made an average of only fifty-four miles a day, although at the start I managed much more and must have averaged thirty miles a day since, except for one day. The wind has died down again.

"It took eleven days for the 555-mile lap to the Canaries. This passage is five times as long and should have taken me fifty-five days, which means, I suppose, that I shall arrive on Saturday.

"There is very little fresh water left, and I cannot face the idea of sea water with this bad diarrhea; am catching very few fish; they must be getting suspicious. This does not really matter, as there are plenty of flying fish. If things come to the worst, I always have my reserve stock of emergency food, but once I have eaten that, it would all be over. Whoever writes a book for cast-aways based on my experiences will have to give entirely different figures for the distance from land indicated by the birds. This one must be hundreds of miles out. Feeling very disheartened, but somehow I must find the strength to carry on. If only I knew my exact longitude. If I were absolutely sure of my position, however far there was to go, I would feel a bit better. The ship and plane routes must lie to the west of the islands, in the Caribbean, which is why there are none to be seen. And to think that I had the sea anchor out for a whole day, while now my sail is drooping uselessly. God, what can I do to end this terrible uncertainty?

"The day is going to be unbearably hot, without a cloud to mask the sun. Luck seems dead against me. I can see it raining on the horizon but not a drop comes anywhere near; there are clouds all around, but I get nothing but burning sun. This is supposed to be the regular trade wind season, but I seem to get one day of wind, one with a breeze, and then two or three of flat calm. The dinghy is practically stationary. I can still see my green fluorescent patch after three days; it must be moving with the current, too. And it has been this way since Saturday, the twenty-second, that makes twenty days of near immobility. I am not likely to forget them. I must have been crazy to put any confidence in a book written by specialists. Unfortunately, it looks as if I am not going to live to put their facts right for them. Twenty days of calm when 'the trade wind is at its strongest and most regular'! With this weather I cannot possibly get there alive, and yet there cannot be all that way to go. I keep seeing bits of tree bark and pieces of cork, but my sail is still flapping. Thirty or fifteen hundred miles to go, it is all the same.

"*1430 hours.* This is another day like last Friday; flat calm and a flapping sail. Hurrah for the trade wind! Perhaps this is one of the signs that I am near land, in which case just let me catch sight of it. Outlook for tomorrow: the same. I am not moving an inch. It is now forty-eight hours since I saw my famous group of birds, yet I estimate I must have covered eighty miles.

"*1600 hours.* I must say I would like a swim and a look at the bottom of the boat. At least the dinghy will arrive intact, even if this goes on another month, unless we meet a swordfish.

"*1630 hours.* The sea is rising slightly, proof that there must be wind somewhere, but I am hardly getting a puff. Am hot and thirsty. Please God I live long enough to drink at one gulp two quarts of milk. Think of all the baths I have taken in my life without drinking a drop of the water. What a topsy-turvy world! At home it does not matter whether I turn off the tap or not; here a couple of gallons means the difference between life and death.

"*1700 hours.* Whether I am forty miles from Dominica or not, I shall never get there because there is no wind. [And then in a jumbled handwriting which I cannot recognize as my own I noted:] Another awful day!

"Have run again through my calculations of position:

"October 19, at 15° West, took position at 1215 hours;

"November 14, took position at 1400 hours, a difference of one hour, forty-five minutes, which gives 41° West. This means that by then I had covered 1,568 miles, at an average of fifty-nine miles a day;

"December 8, sun at zenith at 1510 hours; that makes it 59° West, or a run of 1,044 miles since the fourteenth, at an average of forty-three and a half miles a day. That leaves only another 116 miles, so those birds must have been two or three hundred miles out to sea. According to the chart, I should sight something Wednesday or Thursday, at worst Friday, provided I get a little wind, although there is not much sign of it."

It was during this period of dead calm that I had the most dangerous encounter of all. Sitting in the stern of *L'Hérétique,* watching the feeble wake, I saw appear, still some way off, a flat, black, undulating mass in the water. As it came nearer, I saw it had white patches which caught the sun. When it was about fifty feet away, I realized that it was a giant ray. Contrary to all logic, I somehow felt reassured and took out the movie camera to film it, without stopping to think that it probably regarded me as a good meal. It followed me for about two hours, coming no nearer and keeping its distance. Then it suddenly disappeared as if sucked down to the depths. It was only after my return that a fisherman from Dakar told me: "That was probably your moment of greatest danger; the ray could have capsized you with a single flip of a fin or could have leapt clean out of the water on top of you."

"*Tuesday, December 9, 1500 hours.* A slight wind since seven o'clock yesterday evening. If only it holds! Sun as hot as ever today. Had nightmares all night, still nothing in sight; hardly to be wondered at at this rate of progress. Saw three more tropic birds this morning, calling to each other, and they do say that birds make no noise when they are far out to sea. Have drawn up the menu for the dinner I am going to have at the expense of one of my acquaintances who bet me that I would never make it. In fact, I have devised three alternatives: Either *foie gras truffé, soufflé aux crevettes, canard au sang, pommes paille, fromages variés, omelette flambée à la confiture,* and *fruits rafraîchis au champagne;* or else, *homard Thermidor, perdreau truffé sur canapé, haricots verts, fromages variés, crêpes Suzette* (a dozen), *fruits rafraîchis au champagne;* or, even better, *bouquet d'écrevisses,* a dozen *escargots, lièvre à la royale, pommes vapeur* or *cuissot de chevreuil, fromages variés, omelette flambée aux confitures, ananas au kirsch à la crème.* For wine: Muscadet, Pommard 1928, Vosne-Romanée 1930, Mouton-Rothschild 1947, Château-Yquem 1929, Vielle Cure, and a cigar."

CHAPTER 14

Arakaka and Arrival

THE NEXT DAY the miracle happened. It was another Wednesday. By then it was an effort to get up in the morning. I usually woke about sunup, but I was in no hurry to look around the horizon as I was convinced that it would be as empty as ever. I usually continued to lie in my sleeping bag until the rays of the sun, rising in the sky, started to get hot. That morning at about ten o'clock I took a cursory glance outside the tent and then jumped as if I had been given an electric shock. "A ship," I shouted, almost involuntarily. There on the starboard quarter, about two and a half miles away, was a ship on a course which must bring it across my own. It was a big cargo boat of about seven thousand tons, making quite slow speed. There was no sign that I had been sighted. I fumbled feverishly for my heliograph to flash the sun's rays into the eyes of those on the bridge. At the end of what seemed an interminable wait, someone saw me, and the ship changed course to cut across my stern.

My morale had risen at one bound. I was convinced that the ship must be just short of its destination in one of the West Indies' harbors. I had been right all the time; I was near land. I waved my little tricolor flag on the end of an oar. Imagine how proud I was when the ship, as it drew near, ran up a Union Jack to the peak and then dipped it three times: the salute given to warships met on the high seas. I replied by waving my own little flag. When we were abeam, the captain switched on his loud-speaker and asked: "Do you need any assistance?"

"Just the time, please, and my exact longitude," I replied.

"49° 50′."

I was exactly ten degrees, that is to say, six hundred miles, from my estimated position! I felt as if someone had hit me over the head with a hammer. It was more than I could stand. Seizing the scull, I made for the boat, muttering feverishly to myself: "This is it. Fifty-three days is enough. I give up." The captain hailed me again: "Will you come aboard?"

"I will get the dinghy hoisted in; the experiment is over," I thought. "After all, fifty-three days must prove something."

I bumped the ship's side—she was the *Arakaka*, a big passenger-cargo steamer out of Liverpool—and climbed on board. I was met by a short, sturdy man, about fifty years old, who was in a state of considerable excitement: Captain Carter of Liverpool. He asked me straightaway: "Would you like us to take you and your equipment on board? We are making for Georgetown, British Guiana."

My first reaction was to answer yes, but then I remembered my experience with the *Sidi Ferruch*. I thought of my friends, and the seafaring folk at Boulogne who would say: "So you didn't get across the Atlantic after all."

The fifty-three days the voyage had lasted would have served no purpose. Although I had sufficiently proved my theory, the man in the street, or rather the ordinary seaman, would regard my giving up at this point as invalidating the whole experiment. If I was to be instrumental in saving all those human lives, then my voyage had to be completed. Only thus could I render a real service to the world of the sea. I pulled myself together and asked the captain for a few minutes to make up my mind. In the meantime, he offered me a fresh-water shower, which I accepted with gratitude. While I let the delicious water run over me, I heard one officer remark to another in the passage:

"You have to hand it to the French. They will try anything."

That did it. I would go on. I made a quick mental calculation and realized that at my present speed I would need another twenty days to reach land. It was then December 10, which meant arriving about January 3. In order to take my position with certainty I was going to need the *Pilot Book* for 1953.

The captain came to see me again while I was in the shower and said: "Wouldn't you like a meal?"

I declined vigorously, but he insisted.

"You cannot refuse a hot meal."

It was my first proper meal in fifty-three days. I remember it well. There was a fried egg, a little piece of liver, a spoonful of cabbage, and some fruit. Not only was I to be reproached later for eating it, but it gave me the worst stomach trouble of the whole voyage. I sent off a telegram to my wife and was shown around the ship. I shall always remember the luxurious officers' wardroom, with its leather armchairs. The table was laid for lunch. The passengers lived in solid British comfort. Noting all this, I repeated to myself: "Another twenty days, another twenty days." The captain took me into the charthouse, showed me my exact position, and gave me a note of the declinations I would have to observe as I approached the land. He gave me a *Pilot Book,* with the 1953 figures, and presented me with a copy of the superb *British Admiralty Sailing Instructions,* which he auto-graphed.

Then, crossing the deck with slightly uncertain steps, but still perfectly firm on my feet, I made for the rail, where they had put down a Jacob's ladder for me to return to *L'Hérétique.* Most of the crew were there to cheer me on, promising to meet again on land. The captain seemed much moved. Just as I was about to go down the ladder he cried: "What can I do for you; you must let me do something. Is there nothing which would be of assistance?"

Then I remembered that I had heard no Bach during the whole of the journey and said that on Christmas night I would very much like to hear the Sixth Brandenburg Concerto. (One of the gifts I had received on board was a new battery for my radio.)

"I'll turn the B.B.C. upside down if necessary," he replied. "I give you my word they will play your Concerto for Christmas."

I dropped the towline, and the *Arakaka* waited for me to stand off a little before starting her engines, so that my fragile craft should not be sucked into the powerful propellers. A light breeze had sprung up, and I was in a hurry to take advantage of it, so I hoisted my sail and set course for the west. Our meeting had lasted an hour and a half. The *Arakaka* slowly gathered way and, amidst the bellowing of her siren, dipped her flag three times again in salute.

I knew that I was going to regret the *Arakaka* and that sometimes I was going to think: "Why did I not take advantage of the captain's offer; it was probably my last chance?" But for my experiment to be a success, it was absolutely essential for me to press on. In the end, it was the decision of which I was most proud. The entry in my logbook that day read:

"Wednesday, December 10. Wednesday must be my lucky day. I have just been on board a ship, have had a light meal, and am on my way again. Alas, I am only on the fiftieth meridian and have another six hundred miles to go. At this speed I shall need another fifteen or twenty days. Morale high, but I still have it in for the specialists. Now at least I know how to take my longitude; cannot think how I timed my first sight at 1215 hours when it must have been at least 1300. The noon sun will now give me my true position. Ginette has had a message and the voyage continues. God is good. It was the cargo steamer *Arakaka*. Captain Carter, out of Liverpool, destination Guiana. I have to admit I very nearly stayed on board."

Actually, only the merest chance could have brought about such a meeting in that part of the ocean. I might quite easily have continued on my voyage without seeing a thing. In that case, it is more than likely that I would have gone mad. Convinced of my proximity to land, I had been spending more and more of my time scanning the horizon, tiring my eyes and wearing myself out and becoming a little more demoralized each day. The blessed *Arakaka* not only saved me by reassuring my family, but raised my morale. At last I knew where I was and could determine my longitude with precision. The captain had pointed out to me in the *Pilot Book,* a little table, called the time equation, which supplied a small correction to subtract from the hour the sun reached its zenith. As long as I could determine this time, I could not be more than sixty miles out in my calculations. I could now navigate with confidence: my watch had been put right and the new radio battery I had been so kindly given enabled me to make a further check.

That day and for some days following I had no appetite for fish; unfortunately, that was all there was to eat. The snack I had eaten on board *Arakaka* was having its effect. In due course, back in Paris again, a famous expert on nutrition told me: "If we had known you had a meal on the ship you met, we would not have rated your chances of survival very high." What now happened to me was identical with the experience of political deportees and liberated prisoners of war. I had taken two forms of nourishment. Before my little meal on the fifty-third day, my food had been abnormal. Afterward, losing all appetite for fish, I became undernourished. The human organism gradually accustoms itself to a change and diminution in the normal ration, but after a proper meal, the digestive system seems to say: "There, things are back to normal again. I need to make no further special effort," rather like an athlete who stops in the middle of a race and finds he cannot start again. The stomach becomes prey to a sort of despair. I lost more weight (the photographs prove it) during the twelve days still remaining to land than in the fifty-three days prior to my meeting with the *Arakaka*.

I had now made up my mind about the value of books written for the benefit of castaways, with all their hints on navigation, signs that land is near, and all the evidence of floating timber, butterflies, gossamer threads, flies, and birds. Do not take it too hard, dear author of the raft book; whether the frigate bird can spend a night at sea or not, I do not know, but it is certainly to be found fifteen hundred miles from land. It is also incorrect to say that it does not catch its own fish, as I have seen them swoop down on the flying fish chased out of the sea by the dolphins.

How had I managed to make such hopeless miscalculations of my position? I took my first sight on leaving the Canaries in a very rough sea and must have mistaken the crest of a wave for the horizon. By a curious combination of error, I had obtained my correct latitude, but was an hour out in the time. I thought I had determined the fifteenth degree of longitude at 1215, when in reality it was one o'clock in the afternoon. I had therefore concluded that I must make a correction of forty-five minutes, that is to say, a minimum of ten degrees. When I thought I had reached 60° West, I was only at 50° West and still had another six hundred miles to go.

I wanted to reach the French West Indian islands, particularly as they were the only ones with a protected harbor on the east coast. I therefore tried to keep on the latitude of Martinique, always prepared to drift toward Barbados if the north wind persisted. I ran the risk, nevertheless, of being carried to the south of the British island and seeing my route prolonged by some three hundred miles. Three days after meeting the *Arakaka*, I encountered the most curious weather of the whole voyage. As soon as the morning had passed, a flat calm descended again, but an endless stream of little, woolly clouds, quite low, hurried past right above me. The dinghy barely moved. I sat there the whole day in an impotent rage, watching them scudding toward land.

Fortunately, I did not spend the day alone. A somewhat ominous companion, but at least a companion, put in an appearance. A thunderous snort suddenly attracted my attention off to the left and I saw coming toward me a large whale. I feared at first that the beast would come too near the dinghy and damage it with its tail, but although it had several good looks, it never came nearer than a dozen feet or so. It moved ponderously around the boat most of the day and then, at dusk, gravely made off, never to be seen again.

In the meantime, a storm was gathering. About one o'clock in the morning the first big waves started to toss my cockleshell around. The final days were not going to spare me. During the twenty days of storm I had already endured, I had been swamped twice, but I had to put up with four more involuntary duckings during the twelve days that remained. Fortunately, I had perfected my bailing procedure. Once the dinghy was full of water, I started to empty it with my linen hat, five or six pints at a time, getting down to the fine work with a shoe. The most simple methods are often the best for dealing with the elements.

My chief joy was to see the sail filled again to bursting and to hear once more the characteristic hiss of my best speed: about three knots. I had no log, but the noise the dinghy made going through the water enabled me to estimate my speed.

The more progress I made, the greater was my fear that some stupid accident would ruin everything just as I was within sight of success. There was still the fear that one violent wave might nullify at one blow my successful survival of all previous dangers. In a duel with the sea, not a moment's relaxation is permitted, but I still remember my shouts of joy as I felt the wind whistling in my ears.

I finally settled down to sleep quite happily, but was awakened abruptly with the feeling that something unusual was going on. I got up. The sea aft was crisscrossed by the phosphorescent wake of some huge fish. Was it a swordfish or a shark? I never discovered, but it had invented a new and dangerous game. Swimming straight at the raft, it ducked just underneath it at the last moment, rasping the bottom with its back. This went on for six hours. Exasperated, I finally made up my mind to attack it, but the beast disappeared as rapidly as it had arrived. The next morning, although no wave had hit *L'Hérétique* during the night, I found that I was wet through. It was only too clear that the boat was beginning to leak. My nocturnal visitor must have damaged the fabric sufficiently with his sandpaper back to reduce its impermeability. It was high time I reached my destination, as my situation was becoming distinctly uncomfortable. The floats seemed to have come through unscathed and kept up their air pressure. But water was seeping slowly through the whole bottom of the boat and it was impossible to repair these leaks. A proper hole would have been easy to fix. Every five hours or so, when the water reached the deck boards, I had to bail, and this went on during the whole ten days that remained before I touched land.

The birds became more and more numerous and varied. At last, on December 13, the first sea gull appeared. I was back in familiar territory. During the day I was able to film a fantastic scene. For some days, a frigate bird, surely one of the most handsome sea birds in existence, had been keeping me company, diving from time to time to catch a flying fish. I had been puzzling over how this bird knew how to be at the exact spot when its prey took flight. I suddenly realized that it was working in collaboration with the dolphins. These used to make a sudden concerted assault on a shoal of flying fish, scattering them into the air, and then chasing them, often leaping out of the water themselves in the process. As soon as the bird saw the attack begin, it dived toward the pack and came up every time with a flying fish in its beak.

Rising to a considerable height, it would drop the fish suddenly, diving rapidly underneath its line of fall and catching it head-first in its wide-open beak. A quick gulp and it was gone, an almost perfect example of refueling in mid-air. The most extraordinary thing was to see the fish cruising along in parallel flight with the bird.

The light meal I had eaten on board the *Arakaka* had the most curious effects. First of all, overnight, my attack of diarrhea died down, although I half expected the contrary, as cabbage and fruit have a laxative effect. Another result was no less surprising and rather more unpleasant. The meal had restored my normal appetite. It was not until after I had eaten it on December 10 that I began to feel hungry. I suffered thereafter from terrible stomach cramps, although my food supplies were the same and as plentiful as before meeting the ship. I started to yawn like a starving man, something which had never happened in the fifty preceding days. I had nightmares about food every time I went to sleep, with one image recurring like a *leitmotif*: a dish of chicken with rice. I still cannot understand why.

I spent the whole of December 20 remembering all the good meals I had eaten since the war, particularly during the weeks which led up to my departure. Having calculated that, barring accidents, I had about as many more days at sea as my stay at Casablanca had lasted, I tried to remember with each meal of plankton and fish the menu I had eaten on land for the corresponding day: "Today," I was able to say, "I lunched at Admiralty House on *lièvre à la royale;* this evening with the Casablanca Medical Association on *rognons au vin blanc."*

I had at last changed my chart. I had finished with the general chart of the Atlantic and was now marking my position on that of the approaches to the Caribbean. The only drawback was that its larger scale gave me the impression that I had farther to go.

To mark this event I threw into the sea my last message in a bottle. It read: "Experiment successful; mission practically accomplished. Will finder please forward this message to . . ." I wanted to see whether any of these messages would be picked up. As of now, no such news has reached me.

I considered myself as good as there. The day of the twenty-first ended with the appearance in my wake of a fish about five feet long, with a pointed snout and an impressive set of teeth. It was the first barracuda I caught. He eyed me with a hungry look. I was afraid of him at first and threw my little winch at him on the end of a line. This is the method I usually used to scare sharks, which normally made off at top speed. This beast was different and continued to follow me with a menacing air. I then fixed my bent knife to the end of the underwater gun and after wounding him two or three times sunk the blade deep into his body. I thus put an end to this particular argument. Although I give the creature full credit for courage, I did not relish his indigestible flesh. Then, on the twenty-second, when I woke up just before sunrise, imagine my surprise to see that I had just been passed by a large cargo boat. I was right in its wake and it seemed impossible that I should not have been sighted. Determined to send off more news, I let off a flare to make the ship turn around and find out why it had ignored me.

But the vessel continued slowly on its way and I thought for a moment that it had not even seen the flare. Seizing my last one, I threw it in the air, where it formed a bright, luminous trail. This time the ship turned around and came back until I was almost alongside. She was by no means as easy to board as the *Arakaka,* as the sea was much rougher, but once on deck I found out that it was a Dutch cargo ship bound for Port-of-Spain in the British island of Trinidad, the most southerly of the West Indies. I had made up my mind to ask them to advise Martinique and Barbados of my imminent arrival and to see if they would give me something to eat—not fish—to enable me to spend Christmas in a dignified fashion if I should still be at sea. The captain received me in a very friendly fashion and offered me a cup of coffee. My position was confirmed; I was, as I had calculated, at 13° 50′ North, 58° 20′ West. Then the conversation took an extraordinary turn:

"Captain," I said, "how did you manage to pass so close without seeing me?"

"But we did see you," he replied. "We passed quite close, circled right around you, and not seeing any sign of life, assumed that it was an abandoned dinghy and continued on our way. It was only your signals that brought us back."

"No sign of life, sir?" I retorted. "My sail was set, the rudder fixed, my wireless aerial was up. How can you call that no sign of life? Moreover, you recognized me as soon as I was introduced to you. Supposing I had been a real castaway, half dead and incapable of making any signal, would you have abandoned me to my fate?"

As far as I could make out the captain had simply not thought of this and, incredible as it may seem, it had not even occurred to him to sound his siren to see if that brought any signs of life.

The reader should not suppose that this was an exceptional case. We had already noticed, in the Mediterranean, that passenger liners seemed to consider that the necessity of adhering to a strict time schedule took precedence over rescue work. They are no longer ships, but trains running on the sea. Unless a passenger drew the captain's attention to something unusual, the "train" just rolled on.

I clambered down again into the dinghy and, after marking my position on the chart, realized that the end was in sight. I had another seventy miles to cover, on a course of 232, that is to say, to the southwest, to reach the north coast of Barbados. The wind was strong and, after making a rough calculation of my speed, I expected to see the lighthouse on the northern point (a white light with a double flash, at an interval of ten seconds, visible for twenty miles) between midnight and two in the morning.

It was a tiring day. Although I realized that it was highly un-likely I should see anything, I scanned the horizon ceaselessly in the hope of a miraculous early arrival. I slept quite well during the early part of the evening and then woke up for my last watch. At half past midnight, the sky was suddenly illuminated by a bright flash, followed almost immediately by a second. Grabbing my watch, I timed the next pair of flashes: they were exactly ten seconds apart. For the first time in sixty-five days I had regained contact with land; the flashes were the reflection of the lighthouse beam on the clouds. I must have been about sixteen miles from the northern point of Barbados. I therefore had another dozen hours before having to contend with the problem of landing. I could perfectly well have gone to sleep again, but, almost hys-terical with excitement at the proximity of land—I had almost ceased to believe in its very existence—I sat transfixed on one of the floats, watching the regular flashes, counting again and again the time interval between them, each pair seeming a new miracle. Indeed, for me so it was. It took me nearly two hours to con-vince myself that I was not dreaming.

Barbados is one of the most difficult West Indian islands to ap-proach from the eastern side, unless you have a minute knowledge of the coast. The northern part consists entirely of rocky cliffs, against which the waves thunder incessantly; to the south there is a barrier of reefs about a mile out to sea. Although there are a number of passages into the lagoon, no one without intimate knowledge would dare to risk them. During the eighteenth cen-tury it was on this section of the coast that the notorious Sam Lord lured ships to their destruction. He planted two parallel rows of coconut palms, on which he fixed red and white lights to look like the entrance to a harbor. Ships used to hurl themselves on the reefs. Sam Lord then sent his black slaves to massacre the entire crew so that no witnesses should survive. Any slave returning without at least one head was immediately put to death, thus insuring that they gave no quarter. The cargo was then salvaged and Lord became a fabulously wealthy man.

Sam Lord had been dead for two hundred years, but it was still impossible for me to land on that part of the coast. I had two alternatives: either to make for a stretch of about four miles on the northern part of the coast where landing was just possible, or to round the point, throw out my sea anchor in the deep water to the west, and try to attract the attention of the harbor authorities at Speightstown. At daybreak I was surprised to see that I was much nearer the island that I thought, only four or five miles off. My emotions were very different from those at the time of my landing on the Canaries, but my chances of rounding the northern point and avoiding the mortal dangers of the eastern coast were as dubious as they had been on the earlier occasion of September 3.

For the first time during the whole Atlantic passage, I let down my leeboards to take the wind abeam, in an attempt to round the foaming northern cliff. Back in Casablanca Admiral Sol had warned me to take the greatest possible precautions while attempting to beach the dinghy. Perhaps my experience will be of some assistance to future castaways. If I can offer a word of advice, it is this: once in sight of land the worst seems over, but remember the danger of being killed by the very land which promises salvation. Take your time. Impatience can ruin everything. Stop the boat, observe the coast closely, and choose your point. Never forget that ninety per cent of all sea accidents occur on landing. You must choose a stretch where the sea beats less violently, where there is sand or beach and not some murderous rock. The way to determine this is by observing the color and behavior of the sea: little white caps probably hide a reef, so take heed. Make only for smooth stretches without turbulence or breaking waves.

I managed to round the point and then started winking my heliograph at all the farms and sugar factories lining the coast.

Along this stretch, the sea was no longer disordered but roared ashore in impressive long lines of surf. I had covered about half a mile when I had a terrible shock: almost on the beach was a boat containing five men who appeared to be in difficulties. Had they seen me, and was this an attempt to beat through the surf to my assistance? Caught in a wave, the boat disappeared. When I saw it again the five men were no longer in it. I was terribly agitated. Had these men thought I was in difficulties and, in coming out to my assistance, lost two or three lives? I headed in for the shore as fast as I could. When we were within hailing distance, I realized with surprise that they were Negroes who had not even seen me. They were fishermen and had to risk their lives every day in this sea as a matter of course. Sea urchins are their principal catch. As the boat tosses over the clear water, one of the crew dives in, however high the waves, prepared to be carried with his catch two hundred yards to the sandy shore. I was by this time three hundred yards out and had made up my mind this was the point to land, even though it took me three more hours to get there. Now that I had found a stretch of sand my life was no longer in danger. The dinghy was undamaged and all its equipment intact. Before starting my landing operation I took special care to protect my precious log notes, with all the details I hoped would help to save the lives of so many future castaways.

The final maneuver was exhausting for anybody as worn out as I was. As on most of the African and Caribbean surf beaches, the waves do not break with equal force, but with a clearly defined rhythm which varies from place to place. The seventh and the sixteenth are usually the most dangerous and must be met with extreme care. But at this point, every seventh wave seemed the strongest. The wind was abeam, and I turned the dinghy to present the stern to the shore. At the third wave in each series I turned about to gain some distance toward the shore. After the fifth I faced out to sea again to take the force of the seventh wave by the bow. Laboriously, I covered a few yards at a time,

but each successive seventh wave became more and more dangerous. The fishermen who had seen me did not yet seem to realize
that there was anything unusual in my arrival. Soon I was surrounded by three boats and entered into a shouted conversation
in improvised English with their occupants. Then three of the
Negroes plunged in and climbed on board *L'Hérétique;* for the
first time in my Atlantic passage I had a crew, albeit a pesky
one. They ferreted everywhere, examining everything, and rocking the boat from one side to the other. One of them asked me
for my watch, but when he found that its tick was hardly audible,
handed it back with a disdainful air. Another seemed fascinated
by a piece of soap which he wanted to eat. The third pounced
on my binoculars, which he put to his eyes the wrong way round,
solemnly scanning the horizon. When I explained to him that
they were full of water and useless, he started to shake them as if
to empty a bottle to the last drop. Although I was as good as there,
I began to worry about my logbooks and the emergency store of
food, which I intended to deposit intact at the first police station. But I was too worn out to keep an eye on everything. I
therefore made up my mind to find two or three reliable witnesses as soon as I could, who would confirm that I had not
touched my provisions.

L'Hérétique was still about twenty yards from the beach, which
soon changed in color from yellow to black as the local inhabitants gathered. The fishermen tried to persuade me to wait for
the ebb tide before landing, saying that the waves would be less
strong. What they really wanted was time to search the whole
dinghy before those on shore did. But the desire to touch land,
to smell it, to feel the sensation of warm sand under my feet, was
too strong. Knowing that the dinghy would survive the breaking
waves and exasperated by the uselessness of my new crew, I
dived in, swam the remaining twenty yards with *L'Hérétique's*
anchor, and, aided by scores of people, hauled her ashore. The
beach seemed to pitch and toss under my feet, but I was so trans-

ported with delight that the hunger pains from which I had been suffering disappeared in a flash.

Now, for a last word of advice to future castaways. Avoid at all cost too quick or too large a meal on arrival. It would probably kill you. Take all the liquid you like, but go carefully with the solids, sworn enemies of a weakened digestion. Having snatched your life from the sea, do not let the land take it from you. Once safe, a long bout with hunger can become a fight against the greater menace of a surfeit of food.

CHAPTER 15

A *Landfall*

ALTHOUGH THE BARBADOS beach seemed to rock and shift under my feet, it felt like the Promised Land. To this day I do not know how I found the strength to walk across it, but walk I did. I had to keep a sharp eye on my equipment, as the natives seemed to regard the contents of the boat as some sort of manna from heaven, seizing everything within their grasp. In a flash, they emptied the box of cigarettes which Captain Carter's wife had given me on the *Arakaka*. One of them took possession of my underwater harpoon gun, and after asking what it was used for seemed extremely flattered when I made him a present of it. Someone else made off with an old shirt and a third made signs that he had taken a fancy to the watch on my wrist. When I told him it was the only one I had, he pointed to my wrist compass and said: "But there you have another one."

However, little by little, I managed to unload the dinghy, making a separate pile of anything that had been damaged, including a number of things which had suffered at the last moment, as the dinghy had become completely waterlogged under the battering of the final waves. Then, with the help of a few

204

spectators, I pulled out the still-sealed crate of food. When they saw on it the word "rations," they shouted: "Food! Food!"

I saw that it was going to be impossible for me to keep an eye on everything. At any moment I was going to find the food crate broken open, which would have destroyed the evidence for my theory, even if I had salvaged the contents. By then a local policeman had arrived with the information that the nearest station was two miles away. I had to get there on foot. To this day I don't know where I found the strength to make it. But first I had the presence of mind to take immediate steps to prove that my food reserve was intact. One or two of the more intelligent spectators agreed to serve as witness. I chose the local schoolmistress and lay preacher, together with the policeman. Then I handed around my American tinned food. The recipients were delighted and rubbed their stomachs in acknowledgment.

I have been reproached since for not immediately placing my logbooks under seal as proof that I had not falsified the entries. I can only answer such armchair critics by asking how much they expect from someone who had just reached land after sixty-five days of total isolation and immobility. Slowly, pushed and pulled by the natives, drinking a glass of water at every turning, bathed in sweat, and exhausted, I finally reached the police station. The officer in charge was clearly at a loss to decide whether I was a pirate or an exceptionally foolhardy yachtsman, but with the splendid correctitude of the British policeman, who doubles as father-confessor to those confided to his charge, he sat me down in front of a cup of tea and a piece of bread and butter. I had begun the battle involved in returning to a normal diet; I therefore restricted myself to the tea, with several spoonfuls of sugar. The scene outside was certainly picturesque, with the police station surrounded by hundreds of people all dressed in the bright colors so dear to the inhabitants of these islands.

Finally, about eleven o'clock, I received a personal telephone call from Colonel Reggie Michelin, High Commissioner of Police for the whole of the British West Indies. This seemed to cause a favorable impression on the local officer, who then offered me a shower.

The High Commissioner had told me that a car was on its way to take me to Bridgetown, the capital, where I arrived about two o'clock in the afternoon. My first question was to ask whether the yacht *Nymph Errant* had arrived.

"It got here on December 1," I was told. "Twenty-three days ago, but I think it has left again for Antigua to await the arrival of Anne Davidson." Anne Davidson was also making a solo voyage across the Atlantic, in a sailboat—the only woman to accomplish such a feat.

There must have been a slight misunderstanding on the part of the captain of the *Arakaka* when he asked me where I expected to land. I had answered: the Antilles. Now the British phrase for the Antilles is the West Indies. He must have understood me to say Antigua and had sent off a message to that place. Presumably, my friends, the Stanilands, had gone there in the hope of meeting both Anne Davidson and me. However, someone else reported that the yacht was still in the basin.

I was received by the colonel, a typical Briton, young and dynamic, and the French Consul, Mr. Collins. After explaining that I hoped to rest up for a few days before returning to France, I saw another car arrive. In it were John, Bonnie, his wife, and Winnie, her friend, who shouted with joy at the sight of me and insisted that I was to regard their yacht as my home. I accepted with delight and resigned myself to staying rather longer than I expected. They were accompanied by one of the local physicians, Dr. David Payne, whom I asked to give me an immediate and thorough physical examination in order to determine the exact consequences of my ordeal. I was still feeling quite sprightly, fairly steady on my legs, and even managed to walk around and climb a few stairs. It was only during the days that followed that

I started to pay for the immobility, protracted solitude, and abnormal life I had just experienced.

I complied with the Customs formalities and then sent messages
off to France through the charming Consul. By six o'clock in the
afternoon, I was on board the *Nymph Errant*, where I had to
cope again with the problem of food, as I had decided to take
nothing but liquid nourishment for at least a week. I retired to
my cabin in a state of nervous exhaustion, but found it impossible to sleep. I started tinkering with my radio, taking off the
nylon cover which had protected it and cleaning the parts so that
I could take it back in the best possible condition to France.

About ten o'clock I tried to tune it in to the B.B.C., and to the
stupefaction of my friends we heard the announcer of the B.B.C.
Overseas Service say in French:

"Doctor Bombard, we have received the message from the
captain of the *Arakaka*. We wish to express our appreciation of
your work on behalf of castaways and the hope that this message
reaches you somewhere at sea in *L'Hérétique*. We shall be playing for you tomorrow the Brandenburg Concerto at such-and-
such a time on such-and-such a wave length. (I do not remember
the details now.) Please have your set tuned in."

The next day, by then advised of my arrival in Barbados, the
B.B.C. sent me a telegram to confirm that they would play the
Concerto just the same. During the day the two things happened
which gave me the greatest pleasure, apart from the message I
received from my wife: The Royal Barbados Yacht Club announced that I had been elected an honorary member for the
duration of my stay in the island, and I received the following
cable from Captain Carter:

"Congratulations to a gallant gentleman who had so much
courage in his convictions to carry on when safety and luxury
were proposed. Signed: Carter."

This message was always a consolation during the attacks to
which I was subsequently subjected. The man I had met in

the middle of the ocean, a true seaman, had sent me a token of his esteem, admiration, and friendship.

I spent a week of complete enchantment in Barbados, in spite of the cumulative effects of exhaustion, which obliged me first to carry a stick and then to give up walking almost completely. I was driven all around this island paradise, accustoming myself again to the hues of green which the blue of the sea and sky had almost made me forget.

I was most hospitably received by the Governor, who, as a former prisoner of the Japanese, was able to appreciate better than anyone the moral effect of my recent experiences. A flood of congratulatory telegrams arrived from France, and in the streets, the natives, with their friendly familiarity, greeted me at each turn with, "Hullo, Doc."

All this was most reassuring and comforting. I became almost a legendary figure in Bridgetown. The French colony there made me their honored guest. However, it was time for me to leave the enchanted isles and return to France, where Ginette, as she had said in her telegram, and my friends were awaiting me impatiently.

On December 31 the British West Indies Airways Company flew me as far as Puerto Rico. Calling on the way at Antigua, I learned to my delight that Anne Davidson, who had left the Canaries some time after I did, had arrived the previous evening at the little port of English Harbor. I immediately sent off a message to my friends the Stanilands with the news, which I knew would reassure them on her account.

Arriving at Puerto Rico, I was passing through the immigration authorities when, to my astonishment, the American inspector lifted up his arms in horror because I had no visa. It was useless for me to insist that I was only in transit. The Immigration Law had been altered while I was at sea, and I needed a transit visa to pass through the United States. I was unable to continue my journey and had to stay where I was.

The crew of the British plane which had brought me thus far saw to it that I was installed in a luxurious hotel in the town to wait for the visa, which they assured me could not take long. Without it, I would have to return through the British West Indies to Fort-de-France and leave there for home direct. It was no easy matter to get a visa on New Year's Day, as everyone was on holiday. The immigration officers, however, were most understanding and went to great pains. After a twenty-four-hours' wait in the charming city of San Juan de Puerto Rico, I was authorized to continue my journey and given a visa valid for thirty days. I took off under a mild spring sun. On arriving in New York, I found my friend Percy Knauth waiting for me.

The city was in the midst of a snowstorm, and it was terribly cold. I had not felt as frozen in a year, as most of my passage across the Atlantic had been in the tropics. Barely a week previously I had spent a balmy Christmas night stretched out on a beach under twinkling stars.

The air trip had worn me out, and I was obliged to put off the crossing of the Atlantic in spite of the impatience of my family at the other end. I spent most of the days stretched out on my bed in a hotel with the charming name of the White Whale at Sag Harbor, where my friends lived. Nevertheless, I had to be on my way. I took the plane on the evening of January 6. The route was New York—Montreal—Gander—Paris. When we landed at Montreal I was recognized by a group of young French Canadians who congratulated me on my voyage. Camera bulbs flashed all around me, to the great annoyance of an actress boarding the plane, who pointed at me and asked:

"Who is that?"

"Doctor Bombard," she was told.

"Doctor Bombard?"

"That's right, the chap who has just crossed the Atlantic."

"So what," she replied. "I've been across the Atlantic too."

The indignant air hostess abandoned the good lady without attempting to explain the somewhat special conditions of my crossing. During the flight, there was a brief alarm. Something had gone wrong with the heating system and it became so hot in the plane that there seemed a risk of fire. With magnificent calm, the hostess gave no indication to the other passengers that there was any danger. In one of the nicest compliments ever paid to my voyage she said: "If we ever have to put down in the sea, let us hope it is today when you are there to look after us." Perhaps, after all, I had accomplished something.

On arriving at Paris, she pointed out the crowd waiting for me. I felt as nervous as if I were going to take an examination. The plane stopped, the door opened, and I found myself faced by a surging crowd of welcoming friends, who had come to greet my return to French soil. The wheel had come full circle.

CONCLUSIONS

The voyage of *L'Hérétique* is over. Now I have to fight for the understanding of my heresies and their acceptance as orthodox doctrine for future castaways.

Any survivor of a disaster at sea should be able to reach land in as good physical condition as I did. Mine was a perfectly normal case, my health being that of the average man. I have had three attacks of jaundice in my life and several more or less serious ailments due to the effects of wartime undernourishment. I therefore made the crossing with no particular physical advantages. I was somewhat shrunken on arrival it is true, but I got there. It was not a question of living well but of surviving long enough to reach land or meet a ship.

I claimed to have proved that the sea itself provides sufficient food and drink to enable the battle for survival to be fought with perfect confidence.

During the sixty-five days it took me to get from the Canaries to the West Indies, I enjoyed no particular good fortune. My voyage can be considered neither an exceptional case nor a mere stunt. I lost fifty-five pounds in weight and suffered various minor ills. I had become seriously anemic (my red-corpuscle count was five million at the start and two and a half million on arrival), and my hemoglobin measure had reached the safety limit. The period following the light meal I had on board the *Arakaka* was very nearly fatal.

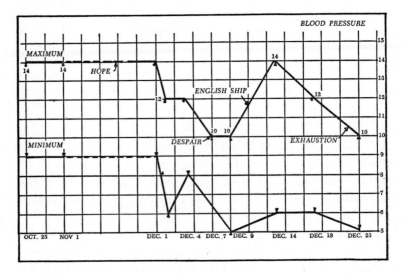

My blood pressure varied greatly with my state of mind. It remained more or less normal until the beginning of December and became dangerously low as my despair increased after that date. My meeting with the *Arakaka* sent it up to normal again, after which it declined slowly with my growing fatigue. It showed clearly the effect on the system of extraneous events and their capacity to cause psychological disturbances and fluctuations in the state of health.

I was wracked by an attack of diarrhea for fourteen days, from November 26 to December 10, with sizeable hemorrhages. I nearly lost consciousness on two occasions: on November 23, when I had the premonition preceding the storm, and on December 6, when I wrote out my will. My skin became dehydrated and I had a rash covering my whole body. I lost the nails from my toes. I developed serious defects of vision, suffered a marked loss in muscular tone, and was hungry. But I got there.

For sixty-five days I lived exclusively on what I could catch from the sea. My intake of proteins and fats was sufficient. The lack of carbohydrates doubtless contributed to my loss of weight, but I had proved that the safety margin, calculated in advance in a laboratory, was a correct estimate.

As an example of the paramount importance of mental endurance over the physical, I need only mention the psychological hunger which I suffered after meeting the *Arakaka*, which had much more serious effects on my health than the organic hunger I endured with Palmer during our period of fast in the Mediterranean. The former variety is not true hunger; it is a desire for something else, always dangerous when it is not available. The latter causes pain and stomach cramp during the first forty-eight hours, which then dies down, to be replaced by somnolence and general weakness. In the first period the organism is burning itself away and in the second it goes into a sort of hibernation.

The medical examination which I had on my arrival gave no indication of any condition caused by avitaminosis. The plankton must therefore have been a sufficient source of Vitamin C.

I had no rain water for the first twenty-three days. During the whole of that period I proved conclusively that I could quench my thirst from fish and that the sea itself provides the liquid necessary to health. After leaving Monaco, I drank sea water for fourteen days in all and fish juice for forty-three days. I had conquered the menace of thirst at sea.

I had been told that sea water was laxative, but during the long period of our Mediterranean fast neither Palmer nor I had a single movement for eleven days. There was no sign of the predicted autointoxication and my mucous membranes never became dry. I shall give a full account of my medical conclusions in the thesis I am preparing. In collaboration with the French naval authorities, I am also working on a handbook for the use of castaways which will summarize and codify the results of my experiment.

I want to assert most emphatically that a life raft can remain at sea for much longer than ten days. It can be steered sufficiently to carry a castaway to safety. *L'Hérétique* was a craft of this type. I have also suggested certain rules of conduct which will keep shipwrecked survivors actively occupied all day, with their hopes concentrated on the supreme object, that of survival. Even a man in the depths of despair can find a second wind which will enable him to pull himself together and continue.

The bottom of a life raft should carry printed in the fabric a map of the prevailing winds and currents in the world's oceans. Survivors of Atlantic wrecks are compelled by these winds and currents to make for America, whatever the distance. To give them hope and convince them that they will survive their ordeal, I would like to see printed on the map: "Remember the man who did it in 1952."

To hope is to seek better things. The survivor of a shipwreck, deprived of everything, must never lose hope. The simple and brutal problem confronting him is that of death or survival. He will need to bolster his courage with all his resources and all his faith in life to fight off despair.

I would like to add one more thought: A human life should be risked in such an experiment as mine only if some useful purpose is being served. If there are any young people who think they see a short cut to fame in setting off in a raft for America or elsewhere, I beg them to reflect and come to see me first. Led astray by false hopes, encouraged by some initial success, or misled into thinking they are on some pleasure trip, they will not realize how desperate is the fight for life until it is too late and will no longer have the time to marshal their courage. Panic will only set in more quickly for having risked their lives to no useful purpose. There will be other and better reasons for such a sacrifice.

But to you, my brother castaway, if you remain firm in belief and hope you will see, as did Robinson Crusoe on his island, how your riches will increase from day to day. And now I trust there is no further reason for you to lose hope.

ABOUT THE AUTHOR

Dr. Alain Bombard was born in Paris, France, and lived there for the first twenty-five years of his life. He attended the Lycée Henri IV and received his medical degree from Faculté de Médecine-Paris. He now lives with his wife and daughter, who was born after he had embarked on the voyage described in this book, in Amiens. His favorite recreations are playing the cello, preferably Bach, composing music, and the sea. In addition to sailing it, Dr. Bombard has twice competed in cross-channel swimming races.

The Voyage of the Hérétique *has already been published in France, Germany, Sweden, and England, where it became an immediate best seller.*

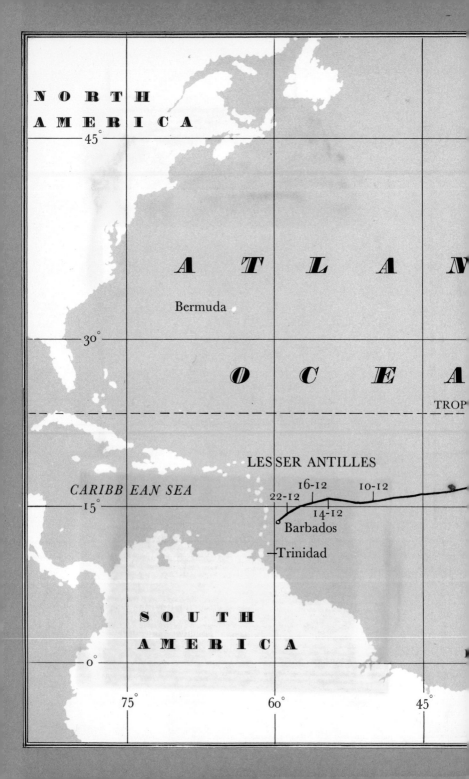